THE BUILDING OF A BOOK

THE
BUILDING OF A BOOK

A SERIES OF PRACTICAL ARTI-
CLES WRITTEN BY EXPERTS IN
THE VARIOUS DEPARTMENTS OF
BOOK MAKING AND DISTRIBUTING

EDITED BY
FREDERICK H. HITCHCOCK 1867-1928

Second Edition
Revised and Enlarged

47599

NEW YORK
R. R. BOWKER COMPANY
1929

TO THE
BOOKSELLER, LIBRARIAN
AND THE
BOOK BUYER
WHO ARE INTERESTED TO KNOW
MORE OF THEIR WARES

FOREWORD

"THE Building of a Book" had its origin in the wish to give practical, non-technical information to readers and lovers of books. I hope it will also be interesting and valuable to those persons who are actually engaged in book making and selling.

All of the contributors are experts in their respective departments, and hence write with authority. I am exceedingly grateful to them for their very generous efforts to make the book a success.

For this Second Edition new articles have been added, and most of the others are completely rewritten or largely revised.

THE EDITOR.

ARTICLES AND CONTRIBUTORS

ix

INTRODUCTION

AMERICA has become book conscious, and, as book sales have increased, the general public has become more interested in their appearance and in the problems facing those who publish, produce and sell them. To meet the demand for information about books, many excellent new volumes on printing and on book collecting have been issued; there has been, however, very little literature on the subject of publishing, and little on book-making from the point of view of the layman as contrasted with the point of view of the specialist.

A number of years ago Frederick H. Hitchcock saw the trend of public interest and printed in 1906 the first edition of "The Building of a Book," bringing together articles from authorities on each problem of the bookmaker. The volume found immediate usefulness but has been long out of print and copies difficult to obtain by those newly come into the book field and needing just this kind of survey. Mr. Hitchcock had practical experience as a publisher and designer of books, a personal enthusiasm for the subject, and knew just to whom to turn for the chapters in his book.

His interest in the subject did not lessen as the years went by, and just before and up to his death a few months ago, he was busy, at the suggestion of his friends, in preparing a revised edition. The material had all been gathered and edited before his death. Every chapter was reweighed, new chapters were added, and every subject reviewed by the original author or someone who had succeeded to an equal eminence in the field. He thus made the book thoroughly up-to-date, as valuable to today's larger group of booklovers as was the first printing to the bookmen of that day.

The scope of the book publisher's office has very greatly broadened in twenty-five years, and Lyman B. Sturgis of the Century Company has, in the first chapter, interpreted present conditions from a varied experience. The function of the literary agent has extended with new markets for the author's output and Carl Brandt in a new chapter points out how the work of the agent fits in with the progress of a manuscript.

With Lawton L. Walton's article on the Manufacturing Department we begin to get a picture of the complicated processes which the publisher must coordinate and direct. He must know something of types and how to choose them, of papers and their selection for varying books, of inks and their composition. All of these basic factors are here described authoritatively but briefly.

The publisher must know, too, the resources and the limitations of hand and machine typesetting, proof reading and its pitfalls, the printing press itself and the way it can be made to give best results.

The field of book illustration opens up a whole new

set of questions for the bookmaker and a new field of delight for the booklover. Line cuts have their special virtues and half-tones their advantages; color can be had by various methods, lithography, four-color, offset. All this information the maker of books must have at his finger-tips.

Before the book is printed the publisher has been planning its binding, and machines fully as intricate as the machines for typesetting and printing, produce large editions or small with amazing quickness. He has been putting his mind also on the problems of publicity, advertising and sales canvas, so that the book may have its adequate hearing.

The resources of the printing press, which underwent so little change in the first four centuries after Gutenberg, have been rapidly expanding in the last half century as the result of research and invention, machinery has been perfected and materials diversified, methods elaborated, and the best modern books will be made by those who thoroughly understand these processes and can coordinate them.

Binding machinery is not one whit behind the machinery of the printer, and a knowledge of the range of the present facilities of these complicated mechanisms is necessary in planning or understanding the modern book.

While the machinery of production has been started up the machinery of distribution and advertising is being put to work, in order that our great potential market of book readers may be given an opportunity to buy.

If all of the publishers' staff, all the booksellers, librarians and the ultimate readers should come to know more about the problems which have been faced in producing the volume which they are handling, the book world would be tied still closer together. If this volume could help to bring such a result, Mr. Hitchcock will have attained something of his purpose in planning this volume, to whose preparation so many of his friends gave their cordial support by valued contributions.

FREDERIC MELCHER.

THE BUILDING OF A BOOK

THE BUILDING OF A BOOK

THE PUBLISHER

By Lyman B. Sturgis

HISTORICALLY speaking the evolution of the book publisher is simple. If the art of publishing is considered to have had its inception with the introduction of movable type by Gutenberg (1397–1468) and Caxton (1422–91), we find that in their early history bookseller and publisher were synonymous, and this remained true even down to the dawn of the nineteenth century. As a matter of fact, the bookseller in many cases was his own printer. The imprints on many early English and American books are sufficient evidence of this. During those three centuries, moreover, a given book was on sale exclusively at one bookstore, or in combination with one or two others, and always confined to one town or locality.

It was only about one hundred years ago that a growing distinction between the publisher and the bookseller —the manufacturer and the retailer—began to be evident, though even today there are certain firms of many years' standing that combine both professions. Improvement of transportation facilities doubtless had much to do with this change, since it brought easier distribution over a wider area from some center, or original source. Today, with the few exceptions referred to, the publisher and the bookseller are quite distinct. Speaking in broad terms, the former is exclusively the manufacturer whose goods reach the ultimate consumer through the retailer, i.e., the bookstore.

It should also be remembered that in more recent times the book publisher is not necessarily his own printer. It is perhaps fair to say that not more than twenty-five per cent of American publishers own their own printing plants. The large majority rely upon outside firms for the physical construction of their books; this includes the composition (i.e., type-setting of any kind), printing, binding, etc.

The first requirements of a publisher if he is to function at all, are manuscripts, the raw material of his industry. Let us, therefore, begin our examination of the publisher's place in the world of books from the standpoint of this raw material, the grist that is brought to his mill.

Manuscripts in great variety reach the publisher from many sources. By far the larger number are submitted directly by the authors, who choose their firms for one of several reasons: it may be for pure sentiment, or because of the recommendation of some brother author, but more often perhaps it is because the manuscript in question is seemingly in accord with the type of literature published by the given firm. A very small percentage of manuscripts so submitted actually prove acceptable for publication, or even worthy of serious consideration. In fact, it is probably true that less than twenty per cent have any real merit, and it is doubtful whether ten per cent are ever published.

Manuscripts are submitted, also, through literary agents whose services have been engaged for practical reasons and primarily to relieve the authors of troublesome detail, delays and disappointments. The agent is of real help to the author if the manuscript must be submitted to more than one publisher before it finds a safe haven. Generally, too, the literary agent is conversant with the details of the publishing business and has an inside knowledge of the current requirements of the different publishers. A capable literary agent is also of real assistance to the publisher, since he is able to sift the chaff from the grain before submitting a manuscript for serious consideration.

Many manuscripts are written to order. A publisher with a knowledge of the public demands and with proper foresight and imagination can often suggest a subject, or outline, for a most successful book. A topic of general public discussion, a magazine article, or an already published volume, may be all that is needed to germinate such an idea. Text-books are often prepared in this way, a competent authority in the chosen field being selected for the work.

Most books of British origin find a ready market in this country. A large number of them are manufactured complete here and this must be done if American copyright is to be obtained. There are also several hundred titles which are imported each year from London in varying quantities either in sheets to be bound here or in their original bound form. There are many instances, too, of an American and a British publisher undertaking some costly book in combination and dividing the original investment. Finally, there are books in foreign languages for which the publisher may secure translation rights by outright purchase, or otherwise, and arrange for a translator.

When a manuscript has been sent to a publisher, what course does it take? Each publisher has a trained and experienced staff of readers with whom rests the chief responsibility. If a manuscript does not seem impossible upon a cursory examination, it will receive the best of attention, often passing through the hands of two or more special readers. The word "impossible" may mean any one of many things; it may denote that the first glance has shown the manuscript to be slovenly in execution or the work of a mere tyro, or in some instances it may signify the publisher's limitations as to the type of literature he is willing to produce. Publishers have traditions, and most of them are inclined to specialize in certain branches of literature,—and particularly those in which some success has already been achieved. There are some firms who will not undertake poetry or drama; the publication of technical books is in the hands of a few special publishers; and there are other firms who confine themselves particularly to religious and theological works. And, finally, a manuscript may be declined at once, because the publisher is already committed to several books on the same or a similar subject—for instance, a publisher has been known to refuse a really creditable mystery story because he had others underway. It is only fair to say, however, what has often been stated before, that no manuscript, whether by a beginner or by an author of known reputation, is slighted by a publisher. It is necessary to stress this point, because it is the common belief of authors and the public at large that no beginner receives a proper hearing. Careful consideration of every manuscript is of primary importance to the publisher, for every one accepted is a part of his stock and trade.

After the readers have submitted their reports, the final verdict rests with a book committee, the head of the firm, or some other responsible person, depending upon the organization of the particular house. Even though the reports are favorable, a manuscript may now be declined,—for quality and intrinsic merit are not the only factors that weigh with the publisher, although recommendation usually means acceptance. Despite real merit and importance, some manuscripts may be refused, if in the judgment of the publisher there is little likelihood of a sufficient sale to repay for the investment.

An offer having been made for the accepted manuscript and mutually satisfactory terms having been agreed upon, the author and the publisher sign a contract, and in a very real sense these two contracting parties are now partners in the venture. If a literary agent is a third party to the agreement, a special clause will cover his interest. All firms have printed forms of agreement, and though these vary in detail, they are alike in principle. Most contracts are made on a royalty basis, a certain percentage of the retail price of the book being payable to the author by the publisher for every copy of the book sold. The author has little further responsibility except to read the proof, though in the case of some books he may be obligated to furnish the originals for illustrations or copy for the index. Photographs for a book of travel or drawings for a book on design, for example, are considered a part of the manuscript. In all other ways the publisher is, as a rule, solely responsible, —for he assumes all expense of manufacture, exploitation and advertising.

The manuscript is usually prepared for the printer by the editorial staff of the publisher some months in advance of the date of publication. Such editorial supervision is generally quite perfunctory, but it is often important because certain standards have been established as to the format and style of his books. This includes, also, uniformity in spelling based on some dictionary of traditional repute, and, in fact, a style sheet is often furnished to the author giving details as to spelling, capitalization, the use of italics, etc. The publisher usually furnishes two sets of proof to the author for his examination and correction.

Though there are no stringent rules, custom has divided the year into two periods for the publication and marketing of new books. The Spring season extends, roughly, from January to May, and the Autumn season, from August to November. The marketing of a book follows along the general lines of those which custom and tradition have made proverbial in any manufacturing industry. The importance of the traveling salesman (with his samples) in any industry is well known, whether he is dealing in buttons or chandeliers. If it is buttons, the complete article can be shown to his prospective buyer; if chandeliers, photographs are employed. It is somewhat different in the book trade, because the buyer often sees a mere shadow of the completed object; he bases his order on a dummy book which is no more than a shell of the final volume, consisting only of a few sheets enclosed in the finished cover. As books are sold largely before they are printed, all that can be shown to the buyer is the table of contents, perhaps a chapter of the text, and examples of the illustrations.

The traveling salesman is equipped, as we have said, with dummies of books scheduled for a given season, and he is also supplied with an announcement list (i.e., a descriptive catalogue) of the forthcoming titles. With these and some talking points the sales force springs into action. We are considering at this point the publisher, or that branch of a publishing house that handles what is vaguely termed a "general line" as distinguished from a line of text-books. The sale and exploitation of the latter will be treated elsewhere in this chapter. A general line can best be defined as comprising those branches of literature primarily intended for entertainment, for general information, or for popular instruction,—such as fiction, stories for children, travel, biography, popular science, etc. The publisher depends upon the bookstores for the sale and distribution of all volumes in this category, and it is to the "buyers" for these stores that he makes his appeal,—in larger cities through the direct contact of the salesmen, elsewhere by means of correspondence or through the intermediary of the wholesaler, or jobber. The latter handles the output of all publishers and represents the "wholesale" source common to many other lines of industry. A new book generally reaches the counters of all bookstores throughout the country on the scheduled date of publication.

The exploitation of a book rests largely on the shoulders of the publisher. For each new book an appropriation for advertising is made, the amount depending upon many factors, and the wise expenditure of this appropriation is what creates public demand and brings the ultimate consumer to the bookstore. The advertising campaign in the first instance is confined to a display in daily newspapers and magazines, but another important channel for exploitation is the book review. Anywhere from one hundred and fifty to three hundred free copies of every book are distributed for this purpose. Where books other than fiction are concerned, circulars are often prepared, and these are usually distributed after, sometimes before, publication to selected lists of names. It is difficult to state concretely what other means for exploitation exist. It depends upon the book and the ingenuity of the publisher. A complimentary copy placed in the hands of a person of prominence has sometimes been of inestimable value; other channels than bookstores may be found for the distribution of some special book; and when a book is definitely established where public approval is concerned, further ways of exploitation make themselves evident.

There are, also, foreign markets to be exploited, and each American publisher of standing has a proper contact abroad, although no field is of great importance except the British Empire, and London is the center of distribution. Many American publishers have offices there, and some few actually compete with British publishers in placing their books on the market. The book of American origin is, however, more likely to reach the British public and the colonies through some established London publisher, who will export from this country an edition in sheets or, particularly in the case of fiction, manufacture his own edition. The Canadian field is generally covered by an accredited agent,—either a resident publisher or a bookseller. The Australian market, when not controlled from London, is fertile ground for our home industry along certain specialized lines. Japan, for instance, is a growing market, but the disposal of American books to foreign countries, other than European, is insignificant. When it proves possible, it usually results in the sale of translation rights for some small sum.

Text-books reach their public in a far different manner. In this connection exploitation includes personal solicitation. There is literally an army of salesmen, representing the different publishers, constantly visiting school principals and teachers, and meeting college professors and instructors. It is these salesmen who secure adoptions for the books issued by their respective firms, and they labor against much competition. Once it is adopted, orders for a book follow automatically and, though booksellers are sometimes made responsible for the actual distribution, this detail in most instances is assumed by the school or college authorities.

The matter of copyright is an important one to the author and publisher alike. In this country under the present law every book must be actually manufactured here if it is to secure the benefit of copyright. In the British Empire and other important publishing centers this is not necessary. In the United States a book is assured of copyright protection when manufactured, published, and placed on sale, provided, however, that a notice of copyright is printed in each copy; it is then required that it be registered at the Congressional Library. Under existing conditions copyright extends over a period of twenty-eight years with a possible renewal of twenty-eight additional years.

The subject matter of a book lends itself to other uses which in other industries would be termed "by-products." In fiction these by-products consist of dramatic production, including the moving picture screen, and what is called "second serial" rights, meaning serialization after book publication. With serious works there is less chance for further use of the text, although serialization after its appearance in book form is not unknown. Many books are reprinted later in cheap editions, and this is especially true of novels, which are nearly always sold and distributed in this form through the medium of some firm other than the original publisher.

The function of a publisher truly has many ramifications, and the detail of the publishing business is overwhelming, but the real aim of every firm is to secure and to hold the good will of the reading public. To accomplish this there must be high standards with respect to the content and physical construction of every volume, and the American standards of today are excellent.

THE LITERARY AGENT

By Carl Brandt

WHEN the idea of a literary agency was first put in concrete form and the agent began functioning, the idea and the agent discovered that they were looked upon with suspicion and distrust by both author and publisher. And it was quite natural that this should be so. The author was asked to pay out a share of his earnings, and the publisher suspected that this share would come out of his pocket. To this was added, justifiably, a general suspicion of any new factor entering an industry which had its settled traditions and usages.

It is due primarily to the foresight, fair dealing, and patience of the pioneers in this calling that the reputable agent of today enjoys almost universal respect and cooperation from both author and publisher. The forerunners to whom the credit is mainly due are Mr. Paul Reynolds in the United States and Messrs. A. P. Watt and J. B. Pinker in England.

In the beginning, the work of the agent was comparatively simple when seen in the light of present-day conditions. At that time an author's chief return from his labor came from his published books. Serialization in magazines and newspapers was in its infancy and only on rare occasions did it occur as a happy windfall. Therefore the agent endeavored to secure clients who were writing books. This remains today as the basic work of the agent because, when all is said and done, book publication is the foundation on which an author's living and reputation depend. All the subsidiary rights which have been developed since are, as their name implies, secondary, even if some of them may pay much larger sums in cash.

Due to changing conditions in the publishing world both of books and magazines, and in some part to the agent's desire to widen his client's market and increase his earning capacity, new outlets were found. With these new sources of revenue the business side of the author's career began to be complicated and this complexity has gradually increased until conditions have been reached as we know them today. Now a successful author, after completing a novel-length work, must cope with magazine serialization, book publication, second newspaper serialization, dramatic rights, motion picture rights, book clubs, and radio rights. Many of these rights are also open to him in England. Still farther there are the rights of translation in many countries speaking other tongues.

Obviously for an author whose success is so great that he must deal with such a multiplicity of detail the services of an agent are indicated.

There are two ways in which, generally speaking, an

agent is responsible for a book's seeing the light of day. The first is in respect to the manuscript of a work already completed and the second to a work which exists only as an idea.

When the agent finds himself in possession of a manuscript which he believes worthy of the serious attention of a publisher he considers carefully a number of factors. It is not enough to secure a fair contract for the book from a publisher—it must be the most advantageous contract possible from the publisher who is best fitted to handle such a work. His decision as to the publisher must be based on whether the publisher is in sympathy with the nature of the work, if he has other manuscripts of a similar kind on his books, and if the author and publisher can work together in amity.

This point decided, the agent approaches the publisher and prepares the way for sympathetic examination of the book. Should the publisher accept it, there is the discussion of terms and the drawing up and signing of the agreement. But the work of the agent is not yet finished. There remains the obligation to see that the author delivers the finally revised copy to the publisher at the time specified, that proof is received by the author and passed promptly, and that the copyright line shall be given to the publisher correctly. Besides this, if the book should also be placed in England, dates of publication must be so arranged that there can be no question of either loss of copyright or discrepancy in time that might hurt the sale on publication.

This brings the operation up to date of publication. At that time the agent must see that the book actually comes out when scheduled, must follow up and collect any advance that may be due, and secure the copies of the book that the publisher presents to the author.

Subsequent to publication the duties of the agent are to receive and verify the statements and payments of royalty which are usually made semi-yearly, arrange any of the minor rights under the contract, and make sure that the reversion of the rights granted under the contract becomes effective when the demand for the book has ceased and the publisher lets it go out of print.

In a large number of cases the agent finds himself involved in the publicity and promotion campaigns for the books of his author. This is a more recent development of agency work and one which is likely to increase. The author's and agent's interests are identical and both profit proportionately to the extent that the publisher is successful in his selling to the public. Therefore any co-operation that the agent can give the publisher is of advantage to every one.

The second manner in which the agent is directly responsible for the publication of a book is the case where it only exists in the shape of an idea.

The development of the calling of the agent, due largely to the wise ideals formulated by the pioneers, has been along two lines. First, increasing the service to the authors and binding the agent's interests more closely to his client's. Second, by playing scrupulously fair with the buyer, the publisher in this instance, making him feel that the agent is an added editorial tool and not a predatory ogre bent on despoiling his bank balance. It is a happy fact that ninety-nine per cent of the publishers have realized this and in many cases prefer to work with an author through an agent than with the author direct. They fee that in dealing with an agent much time can be saved on the sheerly business side of the transaction as the deal can be made without the personal considerations that must be present when negotiating with a creative artist. It must be understood here that the agent generally endeavors to bring the publisher and author into as close personal contact as possible over the artistic and editorial matters which surround the relationship, only injecting himself on the purely commercial plane.

With this condition of mutual understanding in effect between publisher and agent most originative work may be done. For example, the agent is interested in a client who has been writing only fiction and is possibly a bit stale. The agent knows that his client has a hobby or a special interest quite far afield from his regular work, out of which an interesting non-fiction book might be made. He develops a scheme for this book, goes to a publisher, and often gets a definite contract for it before a line is written. The author is benefited by having a vacation from his regular work and the publisher by a new work of general interest on his list.

Again, the publisher has an idea for a book that he

would like written. He talks it over with the agent who searches about until he can suggest the writer who could do the work best. If the publisher thinks so too, then the agent approaches the author and a contract is consummated.

Often too, the publisher finds that his list is weak on some particular point; he needs a distinguished fiction writer, perhaps, or a series of juveniles. He tells the agent of this need. The agent keeps this in mind and when, for some reason or other, such an author as can supply the want is free in the market, he brings them together.

It should be said in this connection, parenthetically, that the modern practice of the agent is to keep an author's work in the hands of one publisher for as long a time as possible. The advantages of cumulative, progressive publication under one imprint are obvious and often outweigh even an offer from another competing publisher which may embrace a decided increase in royalty rate and advances. But, from time to time, conditions do arise which make it necessary to change publishers.

In regard to books of this sort—that is, which are manufactured from the germ of an idea—the detail duties of the agent are the same as they are for manuscripts already completed but to them are added the responsibility of seeing that the author actually writes and delivers the manuscript within the specified time. Sometimes this is no easy matter.

But in general it is safe to say that the agent who most efficiently serves his client is the one whom the publisher can trust not only for fair play but as one understanding his needs and endeavoring to fill them. The ideal sale is the one in which the agent does no selling but brings to the publisher the book he is delighted to buy. It is also true that the author is not best served when terms are demanded which the publisher feels are out of proportion to the earning power of the book. If they are secured and the publisher faces a substantial loss he is not likely to accept and publish enthusiastically the next book by that author. An agent's duty is, I think, to balance the terms carefully. To see that his client receives the top price but which gives the publisher leeway to advertise and promote the book to its best advantage.

The agent has found by experience that it is not enough to sell the immediate book if he is to represent his client fully. He must consider the author's career as a whole and endeavor to estimate what will be the effect of the book at hand on the books to follow. Sometimes, he is forced to advise an author to withdraw a manuscript which is eminently salable as a more important book is scheduled next and the booksellers and critics might get a false impression of him from this work.

As a rule, the agent does not act as an adviser on the artistic side. His function is, after all, commercial. He is the business partner of the author. But there are times when he can give his client perspective on a work that is a bit out of focus. And he does—and sometimes saves a book that would otherwise never be salable.

There are of course obvious advantages which build up the economic *raison d'être* of the literary agent. The manuscripts he submits to publishers must appeal to his trained judgment as being salable not only to the publisher but to the public. This means that one, or perhaps two, preliminary readings have to be performed for the publisher by the agent. Also, he will not send a manuscript on the theology of the Middle Ages to a house which publishes only fiction. Again, he can express frankly and without undue modesty his glowing enthusiasm for an author's work, where the same author would be tongue-tied and silent if he were selling for himself.

Only one more point. In the olden days, kings and princes had whipping boys to suffer their punishments. The agent is the whipping boy of the author and publisher. He is paid for it and likes it because he is able to straighten out many a tangle between author and publisher which would break up between author and publisher not only business relationships but often very old and valued friendships. The matters which concern these two units are complex and bothersome. Often things go wrong and it is only human, especially so with the artistic temperament, to feel a personal grievance. The incident expands and soon there is a real row on. Then in steps the agent. He listens to both sides and because he knows the problems of each, frequently he can suggest a way out—but usually, before all is calm, both of the contestants are quite sure that he was to blame in the first instance. But the agent does not care, his client and his friend are at peace again, and that satisfies him. Then he's off to another storm center.

For myself, I'm glad that chance put me in this business. It has given me the friendship and co-operation of both authors and publishers. I value this the more highly because I believe that they, working together in greater measure than any others, have forwarded civilization, peace, and the appreciation of the beauty of the world and its works.

THE MANUFACTURING DEPARTMENT

By Lawton L. Walton

THE manufacture of a book consists primarily of the processes of typography,[1] or type composition, or the setting up of type—presswork or printing—photo-engraving or other methods of reproduction—designing—die-cutting—and binding, all of which are involved in transforming a manuscript into the completed book as it reaches the reader.

In the machinery of a modern publishing house the manufacturing man is the person who follows these processes in their devious volutions and evolutions, until the finished production comes from the binder's hands.

After a manuscript has been accepted by a publishing house, it is turned over to the manufacturing man with such general instructions regarding the make-up of the book, as may have been considered or discussed with the author, who invariably and sometimes unfortunately, has some preconceived notion of what his book should look like.

The manufacturing man then selects what he con-

[1] The word "typographer" is used to differentiate between the compositor and the printer, the latter being the one who does the presswork.

siders a suitable style and size of type and size of letter-press page for the book, and sends the manuscript to the typographer with instructions to set up a few sample pages, and to make an estimate of the number of pages that the book will make, so as to verify his own calculations in this respect.

If these sample pages do not prove satisfactory, others are set up, until a page is arrived at finally that will meet all the requirements that the publisher deems necessary. This is then invariably submitted to the author for his approval.

This detail settled, the typographer is now instructed to proceed with the composition and to send proofs to the author. Sometimes a book is set up at once in page form but more often first proofs are sent out in galley strips, on which the author makes his corrections before the matter is apportioned into pages; another proof in page form is sent to the author, on the return of which the typographer casts the electrotype plates from which the book is printed, unless, as in rare instances, the book is to be printed from the type, when no electrotype plates are made.

The manufacturing man keeps in touch with this work in its various stages as it proceeds, and as soon as the number of pages that the book will make can definitely be determined, he places an order for the paper on which it is to be printed.

Meanwhile, if the book is to be illustrated, an illustrator must be engaged, and furnished with a set of early proofs of the book from which to select the points or situations to illustrate. When the drawings are finally approved they are carefully looked over, marked to show the size at which they are to be reproduced, and sent to the engraver for reproduction.

Upon receipt of the reproductions from the engraver, the proofs are compared with the originals, and if the work has been satisfactorily performed, the cuts are sent to the typographer or the printer for insertion in their proper places in the plates or type matter of the book.

The matter of the paper on which the book is to be printed has now to be considered: First, the size of the page, i.e., the apportionment of the margins around the page of letter-press, is decided. Second, the quality of paper to be used, and the surface or finish is then selected; and finally, the bulk or thickness that the book must be, to make a volume of proper proportions, is determined. The paper is then ordered, to be delivered to the printer who will print the book.

Time was when paper was made by hand in certain fixed sizes, and the size of the book was determined by the number of times the sheet of paper was folded, and the letter-press page was adapted to the size of the paper. In these days of machinery, when paper can be made in any size of sheet desired, the process is reversed; the size of the letter-press page is determined and the size of the sheet of paper adapted thereto. Upon receipt of the paper the printer sends a full-sized dummy of it to the manufacturing man so that he may compare it with the order that was given to the paper dealer. The book is then put to press, and as soon as the printing has been completed, the printed sheets are delivered to the binder.

If the book is to have a decorative cover, a designer has been employed to furnish a suitable cover design. When the design has been approved, it is turned over to the die cutter to cut the brass dies used by the binder in stamping the design on the cover of the book.

The dies when finished are sent with the design to the binder to be copied. He stamps off some sample covers until the result called for by the designer has been attained and is then ready to proceed with the operation of binding the book, as soon as the printed sheets have been delivered to him from the printer.

The binder is usually supplied by the printer with a small number of advance copies of the book, before the complete run of the sheets has been delivered. These advance copies are bound up at once and delivered to the manufacturing man so that any faults or errors may be caught and improvements be made before the entire edition of the book is bound.

Printed paper wrappers for the book with decorative design or straight typography have been made and supplied to the binder for wrapping each copy, and as soon as the books are bound, they are wrapped and delivered at the publisher's stock rooms.

The manufacturing man sees that early copies of each new book, for copyright purposes, are furnished to the proper department that attends to that detail, and that early copies also are supplied to the publicity department, to place with editors for special or advance reviews.

The manufacturing man also provides the traveling representatives of his house with adequate dummies (i.e., partly completed copies) of all new books as soon as the important details of their make-up have been decided.

This brief outline covers all of the steps in the process of the evolution of a book. Reams, however, could be devoted to the innumerable details that interweave and overlap each other with which the manufacturing man has to contend, when, as is often the case in our larger publishing houses, he has from forty to fifty books, and sometimes more, in process of manufacture at one time. I know of no man to whom disappointment comes more often than to him,—from the delays due to causes wholly unavoidable, to the blunders of stupid workmen and the broken promises of others; but these are all forgotten when the completed book, that he has worried over in its course through the press, in many instances for months, reaches his hands completed, "a thing of beauty."

THE MAKING OF TYPE

By L. Boyd Benton

TYPE is made of type metal, a mixture of tin, antimony, lead, and copper. As antimony expands in solidifying, advantage is taken of this quality, and the mixture is so proportioned that the expansion of the antimony will practically counteract the shrinkage of the other ingredients. The proportion of the mixture is varied according to the size and style of type and to the purposes for which it is used.

Type is cast separately in moulds, a "matrix" at the end of the mould forming the letter or other character.

Machinery is used very largely in modern type-making. The steps of its manufacture are in this order: drawing the design, producing of a metal pattern therefrom, placing the pattern either in the engraving machine to produce steel punches and type-metal originals, or in the matrix-engraving machine to produce matrices, adjusting the matrix to the mould, and finally, casting the type.

The design for a new style of type is made generally with pen and ink, the capital letters being drawn about

an inch high and the others in pre-determined proportions. When the design is for a plain text letter, similar
to that with which this book is printed, it is essential
to have the letters proportioned and shaped in such a
manner as will cause the least strain on the eyes in reading, and, at the same time, produce a pleasing effect
when the page is viewed as a whole. When the printed
page conveys information to the reader, without attract-
ing attention to itself, it is ideal.

While this is true in regard to a design for a text
letter, the design for a display type is often made to attract attention, not only to itself, but to what it pro-
claims, by its boldness and beauty and sometimes even
by its ugliness.

After the design has been drawn, it is placed in a
"delineating machine," [1] where an enlarged outline pencil copy, or tracing, is made, so large that all errors are
easily seen and corrected. New designs may, however,
be drawn in outline by hand on the enlarged scale, thus
rendering unnecessary both the pen-and-ink drawing and
the tracing.

With the aid of the delineating machine, the oper-

[1] The delineating machine was invented by Mr. L. B. Benton, Director
of the General Manufacturing Department of the American Type
Founders Company, which has the exclusive use of this invention. It
simplifies and expedites the work of developing type designs in a wonderful degree. It embodies a principle of mechanics so novel that the
application for a patent was rejected by the United States Patent Office
on the ground that the application described a mechanical impossibility.
After a single demonstration on a machine that had been in operation
several months the patent was granted promptly.

ator, besides being able to produce an accurately enlarged outline pencil tracing of a design, is also enabled, by various adjustments, to change the form of the pencil tracing in such a manner that it becomes proportionately more condensed or extended, and even italicized or backsloped. That is, from a single design, say Gothic, pencil tracings can be made condensed, extended, italicized, and back-sloped, as well as an enlarged facsimile.

The next operation consists in placing the enlarged outline pencil drawing in a machine which enables the operator to reproduce the outline drawing, reduced in size, on a metal plate, evenly covered with wax, with the line traced entirely through the wax. The plate is then covered with a thin layer of copper, electrically deposited, and is "backed up" with metal, and trimmed and finished, similar to an ordinary electrotype plate of a page of type. A copper-faced metal plate is thus produced, on which are the raised outlines of a letter. This is called the "pattern." From this pattern all regular type sizes may be cut. It determines the shape of the letter, but the size and variations from the pattern are determined later by the adjustments of the engraving machine in which it is used.

The pattern is now sent to the engraving room. Machines have superseded the old-fashioned way of cutting punches and originals by hand, and they have enormously increased the production of new type faces. Whereas in the old days it took about eighteen months to bring out a new Roman face, or style of letters, in seven different sizes, today it can be done in about five weeks. The reason is that formerly only one artist, known as a punch-cutter, could work on a single face, and he had to cut all the sizes, otherwise there were noticeable differences in style. By machine methods, where all sizes can be cut simultaneously, it is only a question of having the requisite number of engraving machines.

As to the quality of machine work, it is superior to hand work, both in accuracy and uniformity. The artist formerly cut the punches, or originals, by hand under a magnifying glass, and the excellence of his work was really marvelous. However, when changing from one size to another, there were often perceptible variations in the shapes of the letters, or the sizes were not always evenly graded. By the machine method the workman uses the long end of a lever, as explained below, and has therefore a greater chance of doing accurate work. In addition to this, a rigid pattern forms the shape of the letter, and to it all sizes must conform.

Another gain the machine has over hand-cutting is its greater range. When the old-time artist made an unusually small size of type for Bible use, he did it with great strain on his eyes and nerves. At any moment his tool might slip and spoil the work. With the machine, on the other hand, and with no physical strain whatever, experimental punches have been cut so small as to be legible only with a microscope—too small, in fact, to print. At present there are two styles of engraving machines employed,—one cutting the letter in relief,—called a "punch" if cut in steel, and an "original" if cut in type metal,—and the other cutting a letter in intaglio,—called a "matrix." Both machines are constructed on the principle of the lever, the long arm following the pattern, while the short arm moves either the work against the cutting tool, or the cutting tool against the work. The adjustments are such that the operator is enabled to engrave the letter proportionately more extended or condensed, and lighter or heavier in face, than the pattern. All these variations are necessary for the production of a properly graded modern series containing the usual sizes. In fact, on account of the laws of optics, which cannot be gone into here, only one size of a series is cut in absolutely exact proportion to the patterns.

As it is impossible to describe these machines clearly without the aid of many diagrams and much technical language, only a brief description of their operation will be given.[2]

[2] Mr. Benton is here describing a method of making matrices that was first described in the first edition of this work. He is the inventor of the Punch and Matrix Engraving machine, with the auxiliary machines, apparatus and tools required in a method original with himself, which has largely superseded in all countries the method described in the text-books of typefounding from Moxon (1683) to DeVinne (1914). Although invented for use in type foundries, the engraving machine has its most extensive use in cutting steel punches with which to make matrices for type composing machines. The inventors of the Mergenthaler linotype composing machine and the Lanston Monotype composing machine both failed to devise a method of supplying their machines with the matrices without which they are useless. It was found economically

When the letters are to be engraved in steel, blocks
or "blanks" are cut from soft steel and finished to the
proper size. A blank is then fastened in the "holder,"
the machine for cutting the letter in relief adjusted to
the proper leverage, and the pattern clamped to the
"bed." The long arm of the lever, containing the proper
"tracer" or follower, is moved by the operator around
the outside of the pattern on the copper-faced metal
plate, causing the blank to be moved by the shorter arm
around and against a rotating cutting tool. This operation is repeated several times with different sizes of
tracers and different adjustments to enable the cutting
tool to cut at different depths, until finally a steel letter

impossible to produce matrices in sufficient quantities by hand. By
acquiring Mr. Benton's machine they were enabled to overcome "a
seemingly insurmountable obstacle to their success," to quote the words
of a report to the stockholders of the Mergenthaler Linotype Company,
published in the year following the first use of the machine by that company. Every typesetting machine setting types direct from matrices is
using matrices made by Mr. Benton's invention, or imitations of it.
Mr. Benton's machine is, indeed, one of the "miracles" of mechanism.
It cuts letter punches so minute as to require the aid of a powerful
microscope in reading them. With it, matrices are made containing the
sixty-eight words of the Lord's Prayer on a square which is 1/144th of a
square inch (i.e., the square of 6 typographic points), readable only by
means of microscopes. The same machine is cutting the largest matrices
used in typefounding. There is scarcely a machine or tool device used
in typefounding that Mr. Benton has not notably improved during the
past quarter century. His latest invention (1925) is a completely successful machine for facing printers' brass rule, work which was done
entirely by hand planes until 1916, although numerous attempts to
supersede the hand planes had been made during the preceding hundred
years. Mr. Benton was born in 1844. He was a printer before he
engaged in typefounding. He has been called "the Edison of typefounding."

in relief is produced, engraved the reverse of the pattern and very much smaller. After being hardened and polished, this is called a steel punch, and, when driven into a flat piece of copper, it produces what is known as a "strike" or unfinished matrix.

If in the same machine type metal is used for blanks, the resulting originals are placed in a "flask," or holder, and submerged in a bath, where they receive on the face of the letter a thick coating of nickel, electrically deposited. As soon as the deposit is of sufficient thickness, they are removed and the soft metal letters withdrawn, leaving a deep facsimile impression in the deposited metal, which also is an unfinished matrix.

The machine for engraving a matrix in intaglio is operated in much the same manner as that for engraving a punch in relief. The same patterns are used, but the operator traces on the inside of the raised outline instead of on the outside. Besides following the outline, the operator guides the tracers over all the surface of the pattern within the outlines; otherwise the letter would appear in the matrix in outline only. The matrices are cut in steel and in watchmakers' nickel, and the work is so accurately done that about half the labor of finishing is saved.

It will be noted from the foregoing that all three processes of engraving end in the production of an unfinished matrix.

The adjusting of the matrix to the mould is technically called "fitting," and requires great skill. If type is cast from unfitted matrices, be the letters ever so cleverly designed and perfectly cut, when assembled in the printed page they will present a very ragged appearance. Some letters will appear slanting backward, others forward, some be above the line, others below; some will perforate the paper, while others will not print at all; the distances between the letters will everywhere be unequal, and some will print on but one edge. Indeed, a single letter may have half of these faults, but when the matrices are properly fitted, the printed page presents a smooth and even appearance.

The mould for this purpose is made of hardened steel, and in it is formed the body of the type. The printing end is formed in the matrix. The mould is provided at one end with guides and devices for holding the matrix snugly against it while the type is being cast, and for withdrawing the matrix and opening the mould when the type is discharged. At the opposite end from the matrix is an opening through which the melted metal enters. The moulds are made adjustable so that each character is cast the proper width, the opening of course being wider for a "W" than for an "i." Only one mould is necessary for one size of type, and with it all the matrices for that size may be used. Commercially, however, it is often necessary to make several moulds of the same size in order to produce the requisite amount of type.

After the adjustments are made, the casting of the type follows. Type is now cast in a machine which is automatic, after it is once adjusted to cast a given letter. The melted type metal is forced by a pump into the mould and the matrix, and when solidified, the type is ejected from the mould and moved between knives which trim all four sides. The type is delivered side by side on a specially grooved piece of wood, three feet long, called a "stick," on which they are removed from the machine for inspection. Type is cast at the rate of from one to two hundred and forty per minute, according to the size, the speed being limited only by the time it takes the metal to solidify. To accelerate this, a stream of cold water is forced through passages surrounding the mould, and a jet of cold air is blown against the outside.

The automatic casting machine performs six different operations. Formerly, all of them, except the casting itself, were done by hand, and each type was handled separately, except in the operation of dressing, or the final finishing, where it was handled in lines of about three feet in length.

After the type has been delivered to the inspector, it is examined under a magnifying glass and all imperfect type is thrown out. The perfect type is then delivered to the "fonting" room, where it is weighed, counted, and put up in suitable packages in proper proportion of one letter with another, ready for the printer.

Formerly the various sizes of type were indicated by names which had developed with the history of type making. It was a source of considerable annoyance to printers that these old standards were not accurate, and that two types of supposedly the same size, and sold under the same name, by different makers, varied so much that they could not be used side by side. Of recent years the "point" system, by which each size bears a proportionate relation to every other size, has done much to remedy this trouble, and now nearly all type is made on that basis. An American point is practically one seventy-second of an inch. Actually it is .013837 inch. It was based on the pica size most extensively in use in this country. This pica was divided into twelve equal parts and each part called a point. All the other sizes were made to conform to multiples of this point. The point is so near a seventy-second of an inch that printers frequently calculate the length of the pages by counting the lines, the basis being twelve lines of 6 point, nine lines of 8 point, eight lines of 9 point, and six lines of 12 point to the inch. This calculation is really quite accurate.

The following table will show the old and new names for the various sizes:—

3½ Point	. . . .	Brilliant.
4½ Point	. . . .	Diamond.
5 Point	. . . .	Pearl.
5½ Point	. . . .	Agate.
6 Point	. . . .	Nonpareil.
7 Point	. . . .	Minion.
8 Point	. . . .	Brevier.
9 Point	. . . .	Bourgeois.
10 Point	. . . .	Long Primer.
11 Point	. . . .	Small Pica.

12 Point	. . . . . .	Pica.
14 Point	. . . . . .	2-line Minion or English.
16 Point	. . . . . .	2-line Brevier.
18 Point	. . . . . .	Great Primer.
20 Point	. . . . . .	2-line Long Primer or Paragon.
22 Point	. . . . . .	2-line Small Pica.
24 Point	. . . . . .	2-line Pica.
28 Point	. . . . . .	2-line English.
30 Point	. . . . . .	5-line Nonpareil.
32 Point	. . . . . .	4-line Brevier.
36 Point	. . . . . .	2-line Great Primer.
40 Point	. . . . . .	Double Paragon.
42 Point	. . . . . .	7-line Nonpareil.
44 Point	. . . . . .	4-line Small Pica or Canon.
48 Point	. . . . . .	4-line Pica.
54 Point	. . . . . .	9-line Nonpareil
60 Point	. . . . . .	5-line Pica.
72 Point	. . . . . .	6-line Pica.

PAPER MAKING

By Herbert W. Mason

THE word "paper" derives its name from the ancient Greek word "papyrus," the name of the material used in ancient times for writing purposes, and manufactured by the Egyptians from the papyrus plant, and which was, up to the eighth century, the best-known writing material. Probably the earliest manufacturers of paper were the Chinese, who used the mulberry tree and other like plants for this purpose, and may be called the inventors of our modern paper manufacturing, as they have practiced the art of paper making for almost two thousand years.

In the ordinary book papers of today the materials used are largely rags and wood fibers. "Esparto," a Spanish grass, is used in England to a great extent, but it is too expensive to import to this country, and is, therefore, not used here. Many other materials could be used to advantage, such as "bagasse," the waste material of sugar cane, and corn stalks, both of which make good book paper; also hemp, wild clover, and other plants which have a good fiber.

Only two kinds of rags are used, linen and cotton,

of both of which there are several grades. Linen rags make a very strong paper, and are mostly used in manufacturing fine writing papers, ledgers, and covers for books where strength is necessary. Cotton rags may be divided into three distinct kinds, whites, blues, and colors, and these in turn are subdivided into several grades. Most of the blue rags are now imported from Germany, Belgium, and France; none from Japan as formerly. The whites and colors are bought in this country.

Wood fibers are divided into two classes, the harder woods, such as spruce, fir, etc., and the softer, such as poplar, cottonwood, etc. There are three ways of reducing or disintegrating wood fibers: first, by sulphurous acid or bi-sulphite of lime fumes, which gives the name "sulphite fiber"; second, by caustic soda, which is called "soda fiber"; and third, by grinding. The last is usually only used for stock in very low grades of paper, such as newspaper and wrapping paper; it is rarely used for books. Many persons think that this ground wood, which is merely spruce ground very fine into pulp, is used in book papers; but if it were, the paper would not last long, and would almost immediately discolor on exposure to light and air. There is a theory that no paper made from wood fibers is lasting, and that therefore high grades of paper for fine books should be made only of rags, but this is erroneous, for wood stock and rag stock nowadays are treated and prepared in the same way, and only practically pure cellulose matter goes into the paper.

It would be a different matter, however, if *ground* wood were used for fine papers, for in this stock the cellulose matter is not separated.

Rags are usually purchased by the paper manufacturer in solid bales, which have been graded into whites, blues, or colors. After being opened, they are thrown into a thrashing machine, which thrashes and shakes out the greater part of the loose dust and dirt. Later, they are sorted more carefully by hand into several grades, according to their colors and cleanliness. All the woolens, gunny, buttons, hooks and eyes, silks, and foreign materials are thrown aside. As the rags are usually too large to be thrown into the boilers to be cooked, they are cut into very small pieces by means of sharp revolving knives, to which they are fed rapidly from an endless belt. When cut, they are packed into a revolving kettle or boiler, called a "rotary," and cooked with caustic soda and lime for several hours to disintegrate the fibers, separate the cellulose matter, and "start" the colors. The rags, after coming out of the boiler, look very dark, and are all mashed together. They are then thrown into a tub of water and revolved horizontally by means of a large wheel fitted with radial knives, which tear and bruise them while water continually runs in and out, carrying away the dirt. In a few hours the rags look much cleaner, and a small amount of chlorate of lime and sulphuric acid is run in to bleach them white. After having been thoroughly stirred for a while, the stock is run into what is called a drainer, where it is allowed to stand for several hours to drain off as much water as possible. Liquid chloride of lime, which is used for bleaching, and sulphuric acid is then run over the fiber, which in turn is drained and washed off again. By this time the pulp is white enough to be sent to the beaters, to be prepared for the paper machines, and is called "half-stock."

Wood fibers for book papers are usually treated in the same general way as rags. First, the logs are peeled and are cut into suitable lengths to be thrown into a wood chopper and cut up in very small pieces. If the wood is treated by sulphurous acid or bi-sulphite of lime fumes, it is called the "sulphite process"; if by caustic soda, the "soda process." This wood is cooked in large upright kettles called "digesters." In one case the sulphite fumes are allowed to permeate through the wood under a high pressure, and in the other the caustic soda is put in "straight," and the wood is cooked under a high pressure of steam. This is done to dissolve out all the gum and resins, in order to leave the pure cellulose matter. After the cooking is done, the stock has to be bleached in very much the same way as the rags and washed thoroughly before it is ready for the "beaters."

For "beating," the stock is thrown into a large revolving tub. Rag and wood fiber may be mixed in different proportions, according to the grade of the paper wanted. The stock is then washed a little to be sure that it is clean and white. Water at first is mixed in with the fiber until it is so diluted that it will flow freely;

A Paper Making Machine

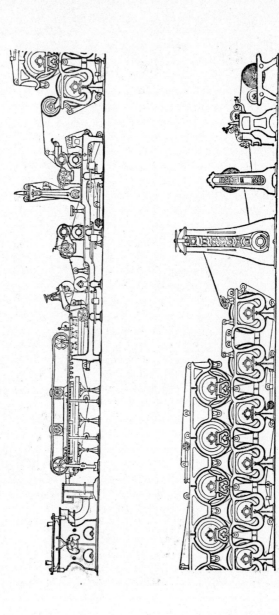

CROSS-SECTION OF A PAPER MACHINE

then it is beaten for several hours by means of an iron wheel covered with iron or steel knives about one-quarter of an inch thick, which revolves over an iron bed-plate with similar knives. During this beating process, clay is mixed with the stock, mainly to give the paper a well-filled and better appearance, and not, as most people think, to add weight, although this is sometimes an object. Sizing material is also added, which helps to keep the fibers together and hold the ink in printing. If it is desired to give the paper a white shade, a small amount of aniline blue or pink is mixed in; otherwise it is called "natural" or "unblued."

The beating part of the process of paper making is the most important. The stock has to be beaten up so that all the fibers are separated and broken into just the right lengths according to the weight and strength of the paper to be made. The harder the roll is set down on the bed plate, the shorter the fiber will be and *vice versa*, but if the roll is not put down hard, the stock has to be beaten so much longer.

"Machining," may be divided into five processes:—

First. When the stock leaves the beater it is run into a large "stuff" chest, and is continually being stirred so that it will not be lumpy. By this time the pulp is about as clean as possible and is ready for the paper machines. The first thing to be done on the machine is to dilute the stock with pure water to the consistency of buttermilk, according to the thickness of the paper required. Then this liquid stock runs through what are called "sand settlers," which are supposed to collect what dirt, iron, etc., remain.

Second. From the sand settlers the stock runs on to a screen, through which it is drawn by means of suction. This process prevents fibers which are lumpy and too long from getting on to the machine, and allows only those of a certain size and length to go forward to be made into paper. An endless and very fine wire cloth, which is continually moving at the same rate of speed as the rest of the paper machine, takes the stock after it has been screened. This is the first step toward making the material into actual paper. Thick rubber straps on each side of the wire determine the width of the paper. The wire shakes a little in order to weave the fibers together while in a state of suspension. At this period the stock looks like thick cream, but soon changes its appearance to the form of a sheet more or less solid on coming to the end of the wire, where there is what is called a "dandy,"—a roll covered with similar wire cloth pressing lightly on the paper as it runs along the wire. Designs in relief on the surface of this roll produce the well-known marks called "water marks." Just beyond the "dandy," underneath the wire, is a suction box which draws enough of the water out so that the paper can go through the "couch" roll at the end of the wire without being crumbled.

Third. The couch roll is a small hard roll covered with a thick felt called a "jacket," and is used on the paper machine to prevent the paper from being crushed, for it presses out much of the water and flattens the paper so that it will pass from the wire to the felts without breaking and through the press rolls without crushing. From this couch roll the paper leaves the wire and is carried along on an endless woolen felt to the press rolls, which are made of hard rubber, steel, or brass. These rolls press the fibers together well, squeezing out more of the water and flattening the sheet.

Fourth. From the press felts the paper is carried to the "dryer felts," which in turn carry the paper to the "dryers," which revolve and by means of the felt carry the paper along to the next dryer, and so on. The dryers are hollow iron or steel cylinders, heated by means of the exhaust steam from the engines which run the machine. More or less steam is allowed to run into the dryers, according to the quality of paper being made.

Fifth. As soon as the paper has been carried over all the dryers, during which time it becomes perfectly dry, it is run through a set of so-called steel "chilled rolls," at the end of the machine, which are under pressure and which give the paper a fairly smooth surface for ordinary type printing. If a rough surface is desired, the paper is simply wound on reels from the dryers.

Super-calendered papers are those which have a high finish and smooth surface, and are used for cuts, lithographic work, magazine papers, and ordinary illustrations. To. calender paper, it is run through a series of alternate "chilled" and "paper" rolls. The chilled rolls are made of steel and have a very smooth and even surface. The "paper" roll is made of circular discs of thin, but strong manila paper, clamped together on an iron shaft, and then put under hydraulic pressure, this pressure being increased constantly until it reaches one hundred tons of pressure to the inch. The rolls are sometimes kept under this pressure for five or six weeks, and then are turned on a lathe into a true and smooth cylinder, and finally burnished by being revolved against each other.

A "cotton" roll, used at times in place of the "paper" roll, is made in the same manner, except that it is made of pieces of cotton cloth instead of thin manila paper. There is a heavy pressure on these rolls, and the paper goes through at a high rate of speed. When an especially smooth surface is wanted, steam is run on the paper as it unwinds, dampening it and giving the web a surface like that on ironed linen.

"Coated" paper is treated differently, being covered with a fine coating, which, after super-calendering, gives the paper a glazed and smooth surface for fine half-tone illustrations. Clay, mixed with casein, the product of skimmed milk, or glue, is the chief material used for coating. It is put on the paper by means of large brushes. Then it is dried by fans and passed through a long passageway heated by steam to a high temperature. After being reeled, it is allowed to stand for a while to harden; then is run several times through the calenders to get the smooth surface. If a high, glazed finish is necessary, steam is put on while running through the calenders. This gives a very bright surface for fine lithographic work. For the best coated papers, instead of clay, sulphate of lime and sometimes sulphate of barium is used, with glue or casein. Formaldehyde, a chemical compound, is used to prevent decomposition in the coating materials; and soda or borax is used to "cut" or dissolve the casein or glue.

If the paper is to be printed "from the web," that is, from the roll, it first has to be trimmed to the correct width, then wound tightly under a high pressure to a certain thickness, then the rolls are packed up in wrapping paper ready to be shipped. Some rolls contain as much as five miles of paper. When the paper is to be put up in sheets, it has to be cut to exactly the correct width and length on the cutting machine. It is all very carefully sorted—the imperfect sheets being thrown out —counted and packed in wooden cases, or done up with strong wrapping paper in bundles, ready to be sent to the printer.

HAND COMPOSITION AND ELECTROTYPING

By J. Stearns Cushing

THE form of the book, the size of the type page, and the size and style of the type having been determined, the manuscript is handed to the foreman of the composing room, with all the collected directions in regard to it. He fills out a scheme of the work which tells the whole story,—somewhat as shown in illustration opposite page 48.

Under the heading "Remarks," in the scheme shown, are noted general directions as to capitalization, punctuation, and spelling (whether Webster, Worcester, or English spelling—which means generally not much more than the insertion of the "u" in words like "favor," "honor," etc., and the use of "s" instead of "z" in words like "recognize," "authorize," etc.). Sometimes these directions are given by the publisher, sometimes by the author, but more often by the superintendent or foreman of the printing-office. The office generally has a fairly well-established system, which is followed in the absence of other orders. It is rarely the case that it is not the wisest course, if one is dealing with a reputable firm of printers, to leave all such details, except deciding the dictionary to be followed, to them. It is their business, and they will, if allowed, pursue a consistent and uniform plan, whereas few authors and fewer publishers are able, or take the pains, to do this. Too often the author has a few peculiar ideas as to punctuation or capitalization, which he introduces just frequently enough to upset the consistent plan of the printer. He will neither leave the responsibility to the latter nor will he assume it himself, and the natural result is a lack of uniformity which might have been avoided if the printer had been allowed to guide this part of the work without interference.

The compositors who are to set the type are selected according to the difficulty of the matter in hand, and each one is given a few pages of the "copy," or manuscript. The portion thus given each compositor is called a "take," and its length is determined by circumstances. For instance, if time is an object, small takes are given, in order that the next step in the forwarding of the work may be started promptly and without the delay which would be occasioned by waiting for the compositor to set up a longer take.

When the compositor has finished his take, the copy and type are passed to a boy, who "locks up" the type on the galley—a flat brass tray with upright sides on which the compositor has placed his type—and takes a proof of it upon a galley- or "roller"-press. This is the proof known as a "galley-proof," and is, in book work, printed on a strip of paper about 7 x 25 inches in size, leaving room for a generous margin to accommodate proof-readers' and authors' corrections, alterations, or additions.

The galley-proof, with the corresponding copy, is then handed to the proof-reader, who is assisted by a "copy-holder" (an assistant who reads the copy aloud) in comparing it with the manuscript and marking typographical errors and departures from copy on its margin. Thence the proof passes back again to the compositor, who corrects the type in accordance with the proof-reader's markings. Opposite page 49 is a specimen of a page proof before correction and after the changes indicated have been made.

New proofs are taken of the corrected galley, and these are revised by a proof-reader in order to be sure that the compositor has made all the corrections marked and to mark anew any he may have overlooked or wrongly altered. If many such occur, the proof is again passed to the compositor for further correction and the taking of fresh proofs. The reviser having found the proof reasonably correct, and having marked on its margin any noticed errors remaining, and also having "queried" to the author any doubtful points to which it is desirable that the latter's attention should be drawn, the proof—known as the "first revise"—and the manuscript are sent to the author for his reading and correction or alteration.[1]

[1] If the book is to be illustrated, the author or publisher should be particular to indicate the position of all cuts by pasting proofs of them

MEMORANDUM No. *1450*

Date: *DEC 10, 1905.*

Name of Book: *The Building of a Book*

Name and Address of Author: *Varies with Each article*

Name and Address of Publisher: *FH Hitchcock*
The Grafton Press
70 Fifth Ave. N.Y. City

Uniform with _____

Size of Page: *3 1/4 × 5 1/2 inches*

Type,—Old Style or Modern face: *Modern face*

Text in *11 point #31* leaded with *12's*

Foot-notes in *8 point #31* leaded with *12's*

Extracts in *9 point #31* leaded with *12's*

Other Types: _____

Running Titles in *11 point caps - Folios at bottom*

Left-hand Running Title: *Title of book*

Right-hand Running Title: *Title of article*

PROOFS to be sent as follows:

1st Rev. and Copy to *Publisher*

(Put Changes of Orders as to Proofs in this column.)

2d Rev. and Old Rev. to *Publisher*

F. Proofs: *In duplicate to publishers*

When begun *Jany 1906* When to be completed: _____

REMARKS.

In spelling & punctuation follow usual office practice.

ADDRESS AT GETTYSBURG

Fourscore and seven years ago our fathers brought forth on this continent a new nation, conceived in liberty, and dedicated to the proposition that all men are created equal.

Now we are engaged in a great civil war, testing whether that nation, or any nation so conceived and so dedicated, can long endure. We are met on a great battlefield of that war. We have come to dedicate a portion of that field as a final resting-place for those who here gave their lives that that nation might live. It is altogether fitting and proper that we should do this.

But, in a larger sense, we cannot dedicate — we cannot consecrate — we cannot hallow — this ground. The brave men, living and dead, who struggled here, have consecrated it far above our poor power to add or detract. The world will little note nor long remember what we say here, but it can never forget what they did here. It is for us, the living, rather, to be dedicated here to the unfinished work which they who fought here

(*Address at the dedication of the Gettysburg National Cemetery, Nov. 19, 1863.* Reprinted, by permission of THE MACMILLAN COMPANY, from "Abraham Lincoln, the Man of the People," by Norman Hapgood.)

ADDRESS AT GETTYSBURG

Fourscore and seven years ago our fathers brought forth on this continent a new nation, conceived in liberty, and dedicated to the proposition that all men are created equal. Now we are engaged in a great civil war, testing whether that nation, or any nation so conceived and so dedicated, can long endure. We are met on a great battlefield of that war. We have come to dedicate a portion of that field as a final resting-place for those who here gave their lives that that nation might live. It is altogether fitting and proper that we should do this.

But, in a larger sense, we cannot dedicate — we cannot consecrate — we cannot hallow — this ground. The brave men, living and dead, who struggled here, have consecrated it far above our poor power to add or detract. The world will little note nor long remember what we say here, but it can never forget what they did here. It is for us, the living, rather, to be dedicated here to the unfinished work which they who fought

(Address at the dedication of the Gettysburg National Cemetery, Nov. 19, 1863. Reprinted, by permission of The Macmillan Company, from Abraham Lincoln, the Man of the People, by Norman Hapgood.)

On the return of the galley-proofs to the printer, the changes indicated on the margins are made by compositors selected for the purpose, and the galleys of type and the proofs are then turned over by them to the "make-up." The "make-up" inserts the cuts, divides the matter into page lengths, and adds the running titles and folios to the pages, following the style of the approved sample pages.

At this stage the separate types composing the page are held in place and together by strong twine called "page cord," which is wound around the whole page several times, the end being so tucked in at the corner as to prevent its becoming unfastened prematurely. The page thus held together is quite secure against being "pied" if proper care is exercised in handling it, and it can be put on a hand-press and excellent proofs readily taken from it. A loosely tied page, however, may allow the letters to spread apart at the ends of the lines, or the type to get "off its feet," or may show lines slightly curved or letters out of alignment. The proof of a page displaying such conditions often causes the author, unlearned in printer's methods, much perturbation of mind

on the margin of the galley-proofs nearest the place desired. The time occupied by the "make-up" in "overrunning" matter for the insertion of cuts is charged as "author's time," and they can be inserted at less expense in the galley-proofs while making-up the type into pages than at any other time. All alterations, so far as practicable, for the same reason, should also be made in the galley-proofs, especially those which involve an increase or decrease in the amount of matter, since changes of this nature made in the page-proof necessitate the added expense of a rearrangement of the made-up pages of type.

and unnecessary fear that his book is going to be printed with these defects. These should in reality be no cause for worry, since by a later operation, that of "locking-up" the "form" in which the pages will be placed before they are sent to the pressroom, or to the electrotyping department, the types readily and correctly adjust themselves.

Proofs of these twine-bound pages are taken on a hand-press, passed to the reviser for comparison with the galley-proofs returned by the author, and if the latter has expressed a wish to see a second revise of the proofs, they are again sent to him. For such a "second revise" and any further revises an extra charge is made. The proofs to which an author is regularly entitled are a duplicate set of the first revise, a duplicate set of page proofs, and a duplicate set of "F"-proofs,—to be mentioned later,—and one set of proofs of the electro-type plates; though it may be added that the last is not at all essential and is seldom called for.

Usually the author does not require to see another proof after the second revise, which he returns to the printer with his final changes and the direction that the pages may be printed, or "corrected and cast," that is, put into the permanent form of electrotype or stereotype plates. Some authors, however, will ask to see and will make alterations in revise after revise, even to the sixth or seventh, and could probably find something to change in several more if the patience or pocketbook of the publisher would permit it. All the expense of overhauling, correcting, and taking additional proofs of the pages is charged by the printer as "author's time." It is possible for an author to make comparatively few and simple changes each time he receives a new revise, but yet have a much larger bill for author's changes than another who makes twice or thrice as many alterations at one time on the galley-proof, and only requires another proof in order that he may verify the correctness of the printer's work. The moral is obvious.

After the pages have been cast, further alterations, while entirely possible, are quite expensive and necessarily more or less injurious to the plates.

The author having given the word to "cast," the pages of type are laid on a smooth, level table of iron or marble called an "imposing stone." They are then enclosed—either two or three or four pages together, according to their size—in iron frames called "chases," in which they are squarely and securely "locked up," the type having first been leveled down by light blows of a mallet on a block of smooth, hard wood called a "planer." This locking-up of the pages in iron frames naturally corrects the defects noted in the twine-bound pages, and not only brings the type into proper alignment and adjustment, but prevents the probability of types becoming displaced or new errors occurring through types dropping out of the page and being wrongly replaced.

When the locking-up process is completed, the iron chase and type embraced by it is called a "form." A proof of this form is read and examined by a proof-reader with the utmost care, with a view to eliminating any remaining errors or defective types or badly adjusted lines, and to making the pages as nearly typographically perfect as possible. It is surprising how many glaring errors, which have eluded all readers up to this time, are discovered by the practiced eye of the final proof-reader.

The form having received this most careful final reading, the proof is passed back to the "stone-hands"—those who lock up and correct the forms—for final correction and adjustment, after which several more sets of proofs are taken, called "F"-proofs (variously and correctly understood as standing for "final," "file," or "foundry" proofs). A set of F-proofs is sent to the author to keep on file, occasionally one is sent to the publisher, and one set is always retained in the proof-room of the printing-office. These proofs are characterized by heavy black borders which enclose each page, and which frequently render nervous authors apprehensive lest their books are to appear in this funereal livery. These black borders are the prints of the "guard-lines," which, rising to the level of the type, form a protection to the pages and the plates in their progress through the electrotyping department; but before the plates are finished up and made ready for the pressroom, the guard-lines, which have been moulded with the type, are removed.

After several sets of F-proofs have been taken, the form is carried to the moulding or "battery" room of the electrotyping department, where it leaves its perfect impress in the receptive wax. Thence it will later be returned to the composing room and taken apart and the type distributed or melted up, soon to be again set up in new combinations of letters and words. The little types making a page of verse today may do duty tomorrow in a page of a text-book in the higher mathematics.

After the type form has been warmed by placing it upon a steam table, an impression of it is taken in a composition resembling wax which is spread upon a metal slab to the thickness of about one-twelfth of an inch. Both the surface of the type and of the wax are thoroughly coated with plumbago or black lead, which serves as a lubricant to prevent the wax from adhering to the type.

As the blank places in the form would not provide sufficient depth in the plate, it is necessary to build them up in the wax mould by dropping more melted wax in such places to a height corresponding to the depth required in the plate, which is, of course, the reverse of the mould, and will show corresponding depressions wherever the mould has raised parts. If great care is not taken in this operation of "building-up," wax is apt to flow over into depressions in the mould, thereby effacing from it a part of the impression, and the plate appears later without the letters or words thus unintentionally blotted out. The reviser of the plate-proofs must watch carefully for such cases.

The mould is now thoroughly brushed over again

with a better quality of black lead than before, and this furnishes the necessary metallic surface without which the copper would not deposit. Then it is "stopped out" by going over its edges with a hot iron, which melts the wax, destroys the black-lead coating, and confines the deposit of copper to its face.

After carefully clearing the face of the mould of all extraneous matter by a strong stream of water, it is washed with a solution of iron filings and blue vitriol which forms a primary copper facing. It is then suspended by a copper-connecting strip in a bath containing a solution of sulphate of copper, water, and sulphuric acid. Through the instrumentality of this solution, and the action of a current of electricity from a dynamo, copper particles separate from sheets of copper (called "anodes," which are also suspended in the bath) and deposit into the face of the mould, thus exactly reproducing the elevations and depressions of the form of type or illustrations of which the mould is an impression. After remaining in the bath about two hours, when the deposit of copper should be about as thick as a visiting card, the mould is taken from the bath and the copper shell removed from the wax by pouring boiling hot water upon it. A further washing in hot lye, and a bath in an acid pickle, completely removes every vestige of wax from the shell. The back of the shell is now moistened with soldering fluid and covered with a layer of tin-foil, which acts as a solder between the copper and the later backing of lead.

The shells are now placed face downward in a shallow pan, and melted lead is poured upon them until of a sufficient depth; then the whole mass is cooled off, and the solid lead plate with copper face is removed from the pan and carried to the finishing room, where it is planed down to a standard thickness of about one-seventh of an inch. The various pages in the cast are sawed apart, the guard-lines removed, side and foot edges beveled, head edge trimmed square, and the open or blank parts of the plate lowered by a routing machine to a sufficient depth to prevent their showing later on the printed sheet.

Then a proof taken from the plates is carefully examined for imperfections, and the plates are corrected or repaired accordingly, and are now ready for the press.

Although, owing to the expense and to the fact that the plate is more or less weakened thereby, it is desirable to avoid as much as possible making alterations in the plates, they *can* be made, and the following is the course generally pursued. If the change involves but a letter or two, the letters in the plate are cut out and new type letters are inserted; but if the alteration involves a whole word or more, it is inadvisable to insert the lead type, because it is softer and less durable than the copper-faced plate, and it will therefore soon show more wear than the rest of the page; so it is customary to reset and electrotype as much of the page as is necessary to incorporate the proposed alteration, then to substitute this part of the page for the part to be altered, by cutting out the old and soldering in the new piece, which must of course exactly correspond in size.

As a patched plate is apt at any time to go to pieces on the press, and may destroy other plates around it, or may even damage the press itself, it is generally considered best to cast a new plate from the patched one. This does not, however, apply to plates in which only single letters or words have been inserted, but to those which have been cut apart their whole width for the insertion of one or more lines.

The plates having been finally approved, they are made up in groups (or "signatures") of sixteen, and packed in strong boxes for future storage. Each box generally contains three of these groups, or forty-eight plates, and is plainly marked with the title of the book and the numbers of the signatures contained therein.

The longevity of good electrotype plates is dependent upon the care with which they are handled and the quality of paper printed from them; but with smooth book paper and good treatment it is entirely possible to print from them a half million impressions.

COMPOSITION BY LINOTYPE

By John R. Rogers

THE linotype was not the product of a day. Its
creator, whose early training had never touched
the printer's art, was fortunately led to the study of that
art, through the efforts of others, whose education had
prepared them to look for a better method of producing
print than that which had been in use since the days of
Gutenberg; but his invention abolished at one stroke
composition and distribution; introduced for the first
time the line, instead of the letter, as the unit of composition; brought into the art the idea of automatically
and instantly producing by a keyboard solid lines of
composed and justified type, to be used one or more
times and then melted down; rendered it possible to
secure new and sharp faces on each printing; abolished
the usual investment for type; cheapened the cost of
standing matter; removed all danger of "pieing," and at
the same time reduced greatly the cost of composition.
The story is an interesting one.

In the autumn of 1876, Charles T. Moore, a native
of Virginia, exhibited to a company of Washington re-
porters a printing machine upon which he had been

working for many years, and which he believed to be then substantially complete. It was a machine of very moderate dimensions, requiring a small motive power, and which bore upon a cylinder in successive rows the characters required for printed matter.

By the manipulation of keys, while the cylinder was kept in continuous forward motion, the characters were printed in lithographic ink upon a paper ribbon, in proper relation to each other; this ribbon was afterwards cut into lengths, arranged in the form of a page, "justified," to a certain extent, but cutting between and separating the words, and then transferred to a lithographic stone, from which the prints were made. These prints were not, of course, of the highest character, but this was a beginning; and the machines were used in Washington and New York, mainly in the transcription of stenographic notes taken in law cases and in the proceedings of legislative committees. A number of these machines were built, but mechanical difficulties became so frequent that the parties interested resolved, very wisely, to put the machine into the hands of a thorough mechanical expert before proceeding to build upon a large scale, so that it might be tried out and a determination reached as to whether or not it was commercially practicable. At the head of the little company of men who nurtured this enterprise and contributed most largely by their labors and means to its development, were James O. Clephane, a well-known law and convention reporter, and Andrew Devine, then the Senate reporter of the Associated Press. In their search for an expert, a Baltimore manufacturer named Hahl, who had constructed some of the machines, was consulted, and upon his recommendation his cousin, Ottmar Mergenthaler, was selected to undertake the work, and thus the future inventor of the Linotype was discovered.

Mergenthaler was born in 1854, in Württemberg, Germany, had been a watchmaker, and at this time was employed upon the finer parts of the mechanical work done in Hahl's shop. The contract was that Mergenthaler was to give his services at a rate of wages considerably beyond what he was then receiving, and Hahl was to charge a reasonable price for the use of his shop and the cost of material. The task undertaken, however, proved to be a far larger one than had been anticipated, and the means of the promoters were exhausted long before the modifications and improvements continually presented had been worked out. The circle of contributors was therefore necessarily widened, and indeed that process went on for years, enough, could they have been foreseen, to have dismayed and disheartened those who were there "in the beginning." Mergenthaler and Moore, assisted by the practical suggestions of Clephane and Devine, continued to work upon the problem for about two years, by which time the lithographic printing machine had become one which indented the characters in a papier-mâché strip, and this being cut up and adjusted upon a flat surface in lines, the way was prepared for casting in type metal.

The next step of importance was the production of the "bar indenting machine," a machine which carried a series of metal bars, bearing upon their edges male printing characters, the bars being provided with springs for "justifying" purposes. The papier-mâché matrix lines resulting from pressure against the characters were secured upon a backing sheet, over which was laid a gridiron frame containing a series of slots, and into these slots type metal was poured by hand to form slugs bearing the characters from which to print. This system was immediately followed by a machine which cast the slugs automatically, one line at a time, from the matrix sheets.

It was in this work that Mergenthaler received the education which resulted in his great invention and in due time he presented his plans for a machine which was known as the "band" machine. In this machine the characters required for printing were indented in the edges of a series of narrow brass bands, each band containing a full alphabet, and hanging, with spacers, side by side in the machine. The bands tapered in thickness from top to bottom, the necessary characters being arranged upon them in the order of the width-space which they occupied.

By touching the keys of a keyboard similar to a typewriter, the bands dropped successively, bringing the characters required into line at a given point; a casting mechanism was then brought in contact with this line of characters, molten metal forced against it through a

mould of the proper dimensions, and a slug with a printing surface upon its face was formed.

This was recognized as a great advance and was
hailed with delight by the now largely increased company. The necessary funds were provided and the building of the new machine undertaken. But Mergenthaler
continued active, and before a second of the "band"
machines could be built, he had devised a plan for dealing with the letters by means of independent matrices.
These matrices were pieces of brass measuring $1\frac{1}{4}$ inches
by $\frac{3}{4}$ of an inch and of the necessary thickness to
accommodate the character which it bore upon its edge
in intaglio; they were stored in the newly devised machine in vertical copper tubes, from the bases of which
they were drawn, as required, by a mechanism actuated
by finger keys, caught by the "ears" as they dropped upon
a miniature railway, and by a blast of air carried one
by one to the assembling point. Wedge spacers being
dropped in between the words, the line was carried to the
front of the mould, where "justification" and casting took
place.

Success seemed at last to have been reached, and
now the problem was, first, how to obtain means to build
machines, and, second, how to persuade printers to use
them. The first of these was the easier, although no
slight task; the second was one of great difficulty. The
field for the machine then in sight was the newspaper,
and the newspaper must appear daily. The old method
of printing from founder's type, set for the most part by

hand, was doing the work; a revolutionary method by which the type was to be made and set by machine, although promising great economies, was a dangerous innovation and one from which publishers naturally shrank. They could see the fate which awaited them if they adopted the new system and it proved unsuccessful. However, a number of newspaper men, after a careful investigation of the whole subject, determined to make the trial; and the leaders of these were Whitelaw Reid of the New York *Tribune*, Melville E. Stone of the Chicago *News* (succeeded by Victor F. Lawson), and Walter N. Haldeman of the Louisville *Courier-Journal*. Into these offices, then, the linotype went. To Mr. Reid belongs the honor of giving the machine a name—line of type—linotype, and of first using it to print a daily newspaper. Of the machine last described, two hundred were built, but before they were half marketed, the ingenious Mergenthaler presented a new form, which showed so great an advance that it was perforce adopted, and the machines then in use, although they gave excellent results, were in course of time displaced. The new machine did away with the air blast, the matrices being carried to the assembling point by gravity from magazines to be hereafter described, and the distributing elevator was displaced by an "arm" which lifted the lines of matrices, after the casting process, to the top of the machine to be returned to their places.

The improvements made in the linotype since

WORKING PARTS OF LINOTYPE MACHINE

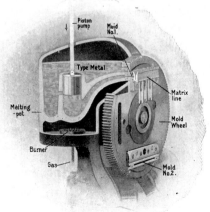

WHERE THE SLUG IS CAST

LINOTYPE SLUGS

A MATRIX

SPACING LINOTYPE MATTER

Mergenthaler's time (he died in 1899 at the early age of forty-five) have been very great; indeed, almost a new machine has been created in doing what was necessary to adapt it to the more and more exacting work which it was called upon to perform in the offices of the great American book publishers. These improvements have been largely the work of, or the following out of suggestions made by, Philip T. Dodge, the patent attorney of the parties interested in the enterprise from the beginning, and since 1891 the President of the Mergenthaler Linotype Company. They went on year after year under the supervision of a corps of gifted mechanical experts, the chief of whom was John R. Rogers, the inventor of the "Typograph," until from the machine of Mergenthaler, supplying through its ninety keys as many characters, a machine appeared yielding three hundred and sixty different characters from the like keyboard. The magazines, too, were capable of being charged with matrices representing any face from Agate (5-point) to English (14-point), and even larger faces for display advertising and for initial letters, by special contrivances which cannot be described without carrying this article beyond reasonable limits. Among the ingenious devices added are: The Rogers systems of setting rule and figure tables, box heads, etc.; the reversal of the line so as to set Hebrew characters in their proper relation; the production of printers' rules of any pattern; the making of ornamental borders; a device for the casting of the same line an indefinite number of times from one setting. The machine was also greatly simplified in its construction.

The amount of money expended in the enterprise before the point of profit was reached was many millions of dollars; but the promoters had faith in the success of the machine and taxed themselves ungrudgingly. Among those who contributed largely to the ultimate result by substantial aid and wise counsel in the conduct of the business the name of D. O. Mills should be particularly mentioned.

There are more than fifty thousand linotypes today in daily use, and the Mergenthaler Linotype Company carries for the purpose of supplying these machines, more than one hundred million of matrices in hundreds of different faces. These matrices are adapted to set more than fifty different languages and additional languages are constantly being arranged so as to be set upon the linotype machine.

At first it was supposed that the linotype was adapted only to newspaper work and the cheaper forms of book and job composition. In recent years much attention has been given to linotype typography with the result that the very finest editions "de luxe" are set upon the linotype machine. Classic faces have been adapted for use in the machine and it is now possible to set any kind of composition, including the finest book work and the most complex composition such as dictionaries, encyclopedias, text-books, etc.

COMPOSITION BY MONOTYPE

By F. L. Rutledge

THOUGH for more than half a century, machines adapted for the setting of type have been in use, it is only within recent years that the average printer of books has been enabled to avail himself of the services of a mechanical substitute for the hand compositor. The fact seems to be that despite the ingenuity that was brought to bear upon the problem, the pioneer inventors were satisfied to obtain speed, with its resultant economy, at the expense of the quality of the finished product. Thus, for some years, machine composition was debarred from the establishments of the makers of fine books, and found its chief field of activity in the office of newspaper publishers and others to whom a technically perfect output was not essential so long as a distinct saving of time and labor could be assured. Thanks, however, to persistent effort on the part of those inventors who would not be satisfied until a machine was evolved which should equal in its output the work of the hand compositor, the problem has been triumphantly solved, and today the very finest examples of the printed book owe their being to the mechanical type-setter.

The claim is made for one of these machines, the monotype, that, instead of lowering the standard of composition, its introduction into the offices of the leading book printers of the world has had the contrary effect, and that it is only the work of the most skilful hand compositor which can at every point be compared with that turned out by the machine. The fact that the type for some recent books of the very highest class, so-called "editions de luxe," has been cast and set by the monotype machine would seem to afford justification for this claim, extravagant as at first glance it may appear.

The monotype machine is, to use a Hibernicism, two machines, which, though quite separate and unrelated, are yet mutually interdependent and necessary, the one to the other. One of these is the composing machine, or keyboard, the other the caster, or type-founder. To begin with the former: this is in appearance not unlike a large typewriter standing upon an iron pedestal, the keyboard which forms its principal feature having two hundred and twenty-five keys corresponding to as many different characters. This keyboard is generally placed in some such position in the printing office as conduces to the health and comfort of the operator, for there is no more noise or disagreeable consequence attendant on its operation than in the case of the familiar typewriter, which it so markedly resembles.

It has been said that the machines are interpendent; yet they are entirely independent as to time and place. The keyboard, as a matter of fact, acts as a

THE MONOTYPE KEYBOARD

The Monotype Caster

sort of go-between betwixt the operator and the casting-machine, setting the latter the task it has to perform and indicating to it the precise manner of its performance.

A roll of paper, which continuously unwinds and is rewound as the keyboard is operated, forms the actual means of communication between the two machines. The operator, as he (or she, for in increasing numbers women are being trained as monotype operators) sits facing the keyboard, has before him, conveniently hanging from an adjustable arm, the "copy" that has to be set in type. As he reads it he manipulates the keys precisely as does an operator on a typewriter, but each key as it is depressed, in place of writing a letter, punches certain round holes in the roll of paper. Enough keys are depressed to form a word, then one is touched to form a space, and so on until just before the end of the line is reached (the length of this line, or the "measure," as it is termed, has at the outset been determined upon by the setting of an indicator) a bell rings, and the operator knows that he must prepare to finish the line with a completed word or syllable and then proceed to justify it. "Justification," as it is termed, is perhaps the most difficult function of either the hand or the machine compositor. On the deftness with which this function is discharged depends almost entirely the typographic excellence of the printed page. To justify is to so increase the distance between the words by the introduction of type-metal "spaces" as to enable the characters to exactly fill the line. To make these spaces as nearly equal as

possible is the aim of every good printer, and in proportion as he succeeds in his endeavor the printed page will
please the eye and be free from those irregularities of
"white space" which detract from its legibility as well
as from its artistic appearance.

That the monotype should not only "justify" each
line automatically, but justify with a mathematical
exactness impossible of attainment by the more or less
rough-and-ready methods of the most careful human
type-setter, is at first thought a little bewildering. The
fact remains, however, that it does so, and this is another
triumph to be recorded for man's "instruments of
precision."

Monotype justification is effected as follows: an
ingenious register device waits, as it were, on all the
movements of the operator, with the result that when he
has approached as close to the end of the line as he dare
go, he has merely to glance at a cylindrical dial in front
of him. The pointer on this dial signifies to him which
of the "justifying keys" he must depress. He touches
them in accordance therewith, and the line is justified,
or rather it *will* be justified when, as will be seen later on,
the casting machine takes up its part of the work. That
is the outward manifestation; it remains to be seen in
what manner the machine accomplishes its task. Firstly,
the machine automatically notes the exact width of the
space left over at the line's end; then, also automatically,
it records the number of spaces between the words
already set which form the incompleted line; finally, it

divides the residuary space into as many parts as there are word-spaces, and allots to each of these one of the parts. Thus if there is one-tenth of an inch to spare at the end of the line and ten word-spaces, then one-hundredth of an inch added to each of these spaces will justify the line with mathematical accuracy. But the machine will do something more wonderful than this. It will separately justify separate parts of the same line. The utility of this is comprehended when it is pointed out that when the "copy" to be set consists of what is technically termed "tabular" matter, the various columns of figures or so forth composing it are not composed vertically but horizontally and so each section must of necessity be justified separately.

Another of the almost unbelievable feats of the monotype is that it will vary the spacing between the different letters of a word. This variation may be accomplished automatically, in which case the space between all the letters of all the words is decreased until the characters actually touch each other, or increased until the page has an "open" effect that is almost painful to the eye. The variation may be accomplished by the operator in the case of specific words or single characters. In German composition, for instance, where emphasis is placed on certain words by having extra spacing between the letters of the words, the operation must be accomplished in hand composition or on composing machines other than the monotype, by actually placing thin spaces between the letters. On the monotype, however, the bodies of the characters themselves are widened or narrowed to add or to take away the exact amount of space previously decided upon.

Should the compositor be required to "over-run illustrations," as the term goes, in other words to leave a space in which the "block" for a cut may be inserted, so that it may have type all around it or on one side of it only, the machine offers no difficulty at all. All that the operator has to do in this case is to carry the composition of each line as far as necessary and then complete it with a row of "quads," or spaces. Thus, when the composition is cast by the casting-machine the space into which the block is to fit is occupied by a square of "quads." These have only to be lifted out, the block inserted, and the trick is done. Or, by a more modern method, the quads can be cast the proper height, and the cut is placed directly on the quads themselves, without removing the quads, and without the use of any other base for the cut.

We will then imagine that the operator has finished his task. Of the bank of two hundred and twenty-five keys in front of him (the equivalent of a full "font" of type, roman, italic, and bold-face, with figures and symbols complete), he has depressed in turn those necessary to spell out the words of his copy, he has put a space between the words he has justified in accordance with the dictates of the justifying dial, has arranged the spaces for the insertion of blocks or illustrations, and as the result of his labors he has merely a roll of perforated paper not unlike that which operates the now familiar pianola or piano-player. Yet this roll of paper is the informing spirit, as it were, of the machine. Its production is the only portion of the work of the monotype for which a human directing agency is necessary, every other function being purely automatic.

The roll of perforated ribbon is lifted off the keyboard and put in place on the casting- and setting-machine. As it is swiftly unwound it delivers to the casting-machine the message with which the operator has charged it. Through the perforations made compressed air is forced. Now, as has been explained, the holes correspond to the characters or typographic symbols of the "copy," and the jet of air forced through them sets in motion the machinery, which controls what is known as the "matrix-case," a rectangular metal frame about five inches square, which contains two hundred and twenty-five matrices, or little blocks of hardened copper, each one of which is a mould corresponding to a character on the keyboard. This frame is mounted horizontally on a slide, which by an ingenious mechanical movement brings any one of the two hundred and twenty-five matrices over what is termed the mould. The particular matrix thus brought into position is determined by those particular holes punched in the paper ribbon at the keyboard, through which the compressed air is at that precise moment being forced.

The mould referred to is closed by the matrix, a jet of molten metal is forced in, and in an instant the type is cast, its face being formed by the matrix, its body or shank by the mould. The cast type is ejected and takes its place in line on the galley, to be followed by another and that by yet others in their regular order. It must, however, be pointed out that the composition emerges from the machine hind part foremost and upside down as it were. This enables the justification holes, which were originally punched at the *end* and not at the beginning of each line, to direct the proper casting of the spaces in the lines to which they correspond.

It will be seen, therefore, that the casting portion of the monotype machine is actually automatic. It performs all its operations without human assistance or direction. Occasionally it will stop of its own accord and refuse to work, but this merely means that it has found something amiss with the perforated instructions, a mistake as to the length of a line or so forth, and it refuses to continue until the workman in charge of it puts the error right, then it starts on again and continues on its even course, casting letters and spaces and punctuation marks, and arranging them first in words, then in lines, next in paragraphs, and finally in a column on the galley.

The casting-machine works at so high a rate of speed (casting from one hundred and forty to one hundred and fifty characters per minute) that it can in its output keep well ahead of the operator on the keyboard. This, however, so far from being an inconvenience or leading to any loss of time, is an advantage, for four casting-machines, which can easily be looked after by one man and a boy, can cope with the work of five keyboard operators, or if all are engaged on the same character of composition two casters can attend to the output of three keyboards.

This suggests a reference to the facilities offered by the machine for the production of matter composed in various faces of type. The machine casts practically all sizes in general use from five-point, or "pearl," to eighteen point, or "great primer." Owing to the number of characters included in the matrix-case, it can at the same time set upper and lower case, small capitals, and upper and lower case italics, or any similar combination of two or even three different faced alphabets. To change from one complete set of matrices to another is a simple operation, performed in about a minute of time, while the changing of the mould, which insures a corresponding change in the size of the "body" of the type, takes about ten minutes.

To return, however, to the perforated roll of paper, which it must be imagined has passed entirely through the casting-machine and has been automatically re-rolled. Its present function has come to an end, and it is now lifted out of its position on the machine and placed away for future reference in a drawer or cabinet. This is a by no means unimportant feature of the monotype, for it is thus no longer necessary to preserve the heavy, cumbrous, and expensive "plates" of a book in anticipation of a second edition being called for at some future time. As a matter of fact, indeed, "plates," or electrotypes of monotyped matter, are by no means a necessity. Many thousand impressions can with safety be printed from the types themselves, and these latter at the conclusion of the job can be remelted and new type cast from the resultant metal. The paper rolls, occupying but a few square inches of space, can be kept, and when the time arrives may be passed through the casting-machine again, to supply a new printing surface identical in every respect with the original.

But the galley of monotyped composition has been waiting during this digression. It is lifted off the machine by the attendant and a rough proof pulled, which is corrected by the proof-reader. The advantage of the individual types is then apparent, for the composition is corrected and otherwise handled precisely as would be the case had the matter been set entirely by hand. Indeed, the operation consumes even less time, for the discarded characters, instead of being placed back carefully in their proper compartments in the case for future use, are merely thrown aside by the corrector, to find their way eventually into the melting pot. It may be added, however, that the monotype itself furnishes the types used in the correction of its matter—"sorts," as they are termed by the printer. These are cast by the machine during the times when it is not employed upon more important work.

As the monotype machine developed, the manufacturing company greatly increased its service to the book publisher and the printer. An attachment has been added to the composing machine whereby, instead of composing type in justified lines, the machine becomes instead a type foundry, casting type for hand composition in all sizes from four point to thirty-six point inclusive. Another attachment for the machine makes it possible to cast unlimited quantities of leads, slugs and rules, from one and a half point to twelve point, either in long strips or cut to measure automatically by a cutting attachment through which the strip is fed as it comes from the machine.

These two features, that of type casting and slug casting, also have been combined in one separate machine, called the "type and rule caster." It is really a private type foundry. More than 3,000 fonts of type matrices and more than 600 rule matrices have been made available by this machine.

Nine years ago the manufacturing company engaged Frederic W. Goudy, the internationally known type designer, as its art director. Book publishers may now choose for machine composition some of the most beautiful letters extant, such as Garamond, Kennerley, Italian Old Style, Cochin, Goudy Old Style, Hess Old Style, Baskerville, Fournier, etc. These artistic faces are all available on the monotype machine, with dozens of others, and many of them are exclusive and can be secured from no other source.

Lately the manufacturing company has perfected three other machines, one called the "lead, slug and rule caster," another the "material-making" machine, both of which are special machines, devoted wholly to the purpose of making spacing material, rules and designed strip borders, and a third, the "giant caster," for making type in forty-two, forty-eight, sixty and seventy-two point sizes and strip metal furniture in all sizes from eighteen to seventy-two point.

It is the usual rather than an exception now, for a *de luxe* book to be composed entirely on the monotype machine,—text, title page, headings, ornaments, leads, rules, spacing material, and all produced from one monotype machine. Important also to the publisher is the fact that the monotype non-distribution system insures that after using, the type will be thrown into the melting pot and used for recasting into new type. This means saving the expense of distributing the type back into the cases, and giving the reader printed pages that are always printed from type that is new, clear, sharp-cut and readable.

PROOF-READING

By George L. Miller

WHEN part of a book has been set up in type, in what is called "galley form," an impression is taken, technically known as "first proof," and this proof is handed to the proof-reader. This long-suffering individual lives in a chronic state of warfare with the compositors on the one hand and the author on the other. His first duty is to see that the proof agrees with the author's manuscript, that nothing has been omitted, and nothing inserted that is not in the copy. He must see, further, that the spelling, punctuation, capitalization, grammar, and so forth, are correct, and the book set according to the "style" ordered. He first of all, therefore, compares the proof with the manuscript, or an assistant reads the manuscript aloud, the proof-reader listening intently for any variation from the proof before him and marking any errors he may find.

Now this seems easy enough, and if every author prepared his copy carefully, so that there could be no possible mistake as to his meaning, nothing would be easier; but in practice a number of questions arise which would never be thought of by an outsider. When a new work is put in hand, if the proof-reader happens to be readily accessible, he is bombarded within the first half-hour or so with, "How am I to spell center?" "Has traveling one or two l's?" "Shall I capitalize the word State?" "Shall I spell out two hundred?" "Do you want ships' names in italic?" and so on and so on. As to punctuation, every compositor thinks he knows better than proof-reader and author combined and often follows his own sweet will. As every error on the first proof must be corrected by the compositor at the expense of the department, here arises the cause of war mentioned in our opening paragraph.

Much has been written about printers' errors and the mistakes of "the intelligent compositor." Aside from those caused by illegible manuscript, mistakes in hand composition come chiefly from faulty "distribution," that is to say, the type has been thrown into the wrong boxes. Thus we get *c* for *e*, *h* for *n*, *y* for *p*, etc., these boxes being contiguous and the letters of the same thickness; if, for instance, the compositor picked up *u* instead of *t* the difference in thickness would at once be noticed by him and the mistake rectified. Then letters are sometimes set upside down and we find letters of a different "face" which have got into the case by mistake. In type set on machine, errors arise from striking adjacent keys, or some matrix will stick in the channel and make its appearance later, sometimes even in the next line. But the chief source of error is illegible, or carelessly prepared manuscript, and to the author's slips of the pen must be added in these days the slips of the typewriter.

It is quite possible for a man to be an expert in astronomy, medicine, or natural history and yet have hazy ideas on spelling and punctuation. "When in doubt use a dash" is an old standing joke, but some authors use dashes all the time, making them do duty for commas, semicolons, and periods. They will write indifferently 4 or four and frequently their capital a's, c's, m's, and n's cannot be distinguished from the small letters. They will commence a story telling that the "Captain" did so and so, and lo, on the next page the "captain" sinks into a common noun; and so with "Father," "mother," "Aunt," "uncle," etc. Just see what the story would look like if set according to such copy!

Now the proof-reader is expected to rectify all this, thereby drawing on his head the wrath of the compositor, who says "he followed the copy," and occasionally incurring the wrath of the author as well for departing therefrom. Sometimes instructions are given that the author's spelling, punctuation, etc., are to be carefully followed, when of course no question can arise; and the proof-reader will query on the proof submitted to the author anything which does not seem to him to be correct.

The great newspapers and magazines have what they call a "style sheet" for the guidance of their compositors and proof-readers and insist on its being faithfully followed. Only by this means could uniformity in the appearance of the paper be secured. In this style sheet careful and minute directions are given for the use of capital letters, the use of italic, spelling out of numbers, compound words, etc. In the Government printing-office in Washington they have a style book of several hundred pages. Some book printing-offices have what they call "the style of the office," which will be followed if no instructions are received from the author to the contrary, while some publishing houses with connections in England insist on English spelling being followed in all their books, as books with American spelling will not sell over there.

Here is an outline of an "office style":—

"Spell and divide words according to Webster's dictionary.

"Capitalize President and all Secretaries of State, Senator, Congressman, Governor, Government (of U. S. or other country), King, Emperor, Republican (and all political parties), all pronouns relating to the Deity, Legislature, State, Nation, Street, Avenue, (Hudson) River.

"Use small capitals for B.C., A.D., A.M., and P.M.

"Use italics for names of ships, names of characters in plays, names of newspapers and magazines, and all foreign words.

"Use quotation marks for names of books.

"Spell out all numbers under 100.

"Compound co-operate, to-day, to-morrow.

"Use period after per cent., and Roman numerals I. VI., etc.

"Bible references in this style: 2 Kings vii. 29.

"All poetical quotations to be in smaller type than text."

Now, some authors will not accept the above style and insist on one entirely different. Many will accept Webster's spelling but draw the line at *theater*, which they want spelt *theatre,* and balk at *skillfully* and *skillful* or *installment*. They will order spelling according to the Standard Dictionary, yet will not accept *sulfur*, *rime*, or *worshiping*. One man wants all his numbers in figures, and another does not like compound words. Still another abhors dashes, or colons, or quotation marks, and yet another will not have italic type used in his work.

So it frequently happens that a proof-reader will have passing through his hands three or four books in entirely different styles, each of which he must bear in mind and conform to if he would avoid trouble. But whatever style he adopted, it is essential that it be strictly adhered to throughout the work; therefore in large printing-offices where there are many proof-readers care is always taken that, however many compositors may be engaged in setting up the work, the same reader handles it from start to finish.

If the proof-reader finds any passages whose meaning is not clear, or sentences of faulty construction, he will call the author's attention thereto. He will also call attention to Biblical or poetical quotations which he may know to be incorrect. Many authors will quote Scripture or poetry from memory, which is found to vary in many respects from the original on verification. And then they complain because "the printer did not set it up right,"—when they are charged for corrections. But why should the compositor bear the expense of correction—or the master-printer for that matter—when the copy was clearly wrong in the first instance? A moment's thought will show the injustice of such a procedure.

From what we have said may be seen the importance of the reading of "first proof." Many offices have the proofs read twice, first without referring to the copy, when the more glaring errors may be corrected at leisure, and then again carefully read by copy. The proofs are then returned to the compositors for correction.

A second proof is now taken which is put in the hands of another proof-reader (or "reviser") for revision. His business is to see that the corrections of the first reader have all been duly made. Should he find any palpable errors that have been overlooked by the first reader, he will call his attention thereto and on approval mark them. It may be necessary to return the proofs again to the compositors for correction, and even a third time. When found to be what is called "clean," they are sent to the author (usually in duplicate) along with the copy.

And now the author sees himself in print, perhaps

for the first time. He will notice that his work presents a different appearance from what it did in manuscript. Here and there a passage can be improved, a phrase polished, an idea amplified—the same man will think differently at different times; and lo, here, the stupid printer has made him speak of a marine landscape when he wrote Maine landscape! (That proof-reader must be disciplined.) And here a sentence has been left out which he wrote on the back of his copy and has been skipped by compositor, copy-holder, proof-reader, and reviser alike! Then the queries of the proof-reader must be answered, and a few commas here and there would improve things,—and so he proceeds to mark up his proofs, for all of which corrections he has to pay at so much per hour—second cause of war.

The proofs are now returned to the printer and corrected, and a revise (after passing through the proof-reader's hands) sent to the author, which process may be repeated *ad infinitum*, until the author gives the order to make up into pages.

The type is now handed over to the "make-up," and inasmuch as his work must be carefully revised by the proof-reader, we may describe it here. Having first of all made a gauge showing the size of the page—supposing the page to be seven inches deep, he will cut a notch in a thin piece of wood showing that size—he must "cast off" or estimate how the pages are going to "break." There must not be any short lines, or "widows" as the printers call them,—that is, the concluding lines of paragraphs which are not full length,—at the heads of pages. The first line of a paragraph should not appear at the bottom of a page (but this rule is more honored in the breach than the observance), and the concluding page of a chapter should not be less than one-quarter page in length. These difficulties are avoided by "saving" a line here and there,—that is, where the last line of a paragraph consists of only one or two words, in squeezing them into the line above, or by "making" lines, which is accomplished by spreading long lines out and driving one or two words over. Any line containing one word only at the end of a paragraph ought to overlap the indention of the first line of the next paragraph. Such a word as "is" or "it" will not do so and should be turned back to the line above. Then again, where cuts or illustrations are inserted in the text a page will sometimes break in the middle of a cut, which, as Euclid says, is impossible, therefore the cut must be moved, sometimes necessitating slight alterations in the text, *e.g.* "The following illustration" must be altered to "The illustration on the next page," or "The illustration above," as the case may be. And here we may remark that all cuts or illustrations should be made and furnished to the printer in time to be inserted in the first proof. The writer calls to mind an instance where the cuts arrived after the whole book had been made up into pages, necessitating a re-make-up at considerable expense.

Proofs of the pages being furnished to the proof-reader, he first of all compares them with the author's last galley proof to see that nothing has been omitted (frequently lines fall off the ends of galleys), that they are in due sequence and "join up," and that the author's last corrections have been made. He then sees to the pagination, the running heads at top of each page, and sees that the foot-notes have been inserted in the pages where they belong and verifies the reference marks. The author will probably have used the * † ‡ § and they will have been so set up, as they appeared on each page of the original manuscript. But when in type and made up into pages they will probably fall differently, the note bearing the § mark may come on the following page and of course must be altered to an *, a corresponding change being made in the text. A much better plan is to number foot-notes 1, 2, 3 and so on, when no alteration on making-up will be required.

The proof-reader must also look after the "widows" and other matters before mentioned. If the book is set in linotype, the make-up will have been unable to make these changes. He will simply allow the proper space and the changes required will be marked by the proof-reader and a number of pages corrected at a time. This is a point of economy.

All corrections having been made and revised, proofs are submitted to the author for his final approval. The author may find it advisable to make alterations even after his book is made up into pages, necessitating further revises; but everything finally being in order, he gives the order to print or to electrotype.

If the pages are to be electrotyped or made into plates, they are "locked up" in an iron frame called a "chase," two or four together, and proofs are given to the proof-reader for a final reading.

If the book is to be printed from the type, the pages are "imposed" in sheets of eight, sixteen, or thirty-two, so arranged that the folios will be in order when the sheet is folded up. They now make what is called, a "form," and a proof of this—known as the "stone proof"—is taken for final reading.

The proof-reader now reads the work all through, looking carefully to the spelling, punctuation, and grammar, as in reading "first proof," and more especially looking out for bad or imperfect letters. If many corrections have been made, the type is very apt to be broken and the spacing between words to become irregular. All imperfect letters must be replaced and bad spacing rectified. Then again, commas, hyphens, periods, and thin letters, such as *l*, *f*, or *t*, are apt to slip out of place at the ends of lines. And here a serious source of error may be mentioned which can be found out only by reading the whole page over. In type set on the linotype machine every line is one solid piece of metal. Any correction to be made involves resetting the whole line. Now the compositor in inserting the new line is very apt to take out a line *beginning with the same word*, replacing it with the new one, thus making a very serious blunder, and of course the proof-reader or author who sees the next proof has no intimation that the wrong line has been tampered with. On reading the page over, however, it will be noticed that something is wrong, previous proofs can be referred to, and the mistake rectified.

The proofs having been finally read, revised, and marked O. K., the pages are sent to the foundry or to press, as the case may be.

But the proof-reader has not done with them yet. If the book is electrotyped, the plates may turn out faulty; sometimes the type will sink in places under the enormous pressure applied in moulding. It is therefore highly advisable that proofs should be taken of the plates and gone over for imperfections; this may save valuable time later when the book is on the press. Some authors don't mind the expense of making changes in their work even after the pages are cast.

The proof-reader only takes leave of the book when it is on the press and all is ready to go ahead and print. A sheet is submitted to him which he must *visé* for bad letters, see that nothing has fallen out in transit to the pressroom, and that the pressman has not taken out any cuts to underlay and reinserted them upside down. He will also verify the folios again (if the book is printed from plates this will be the first opportunity of doing so) and see that the pages join up to what has gone before. Here his work ends.

PRESSWORK

By Walter J. Berwick,

with Revisions by Harold Cadmus

BOOKS are printed in "forms," or sheets, of four, eight, twelve, twenty-four, or thirty-two pages at a time, the number being determined to a great extent by the size of the type page and by the class of the work.

An ordinary twelvemo book, without illustrations in the text, is usually printed in forms of thirty-two pages, on what is known as a single-cylinder flat-bed press, which prints only one side of the paper at an impression. For large editions, the size of the sheet of paper is sometimes doubled and sixty-four pages printed at a time. The class of work in question may also be printed on perfecting presses which print both sides of the paper at one time, and in this way as many as one hundred and twenty-eight pages are frequently printed on one sheet, there being sixty-four pages on each side. Large editions of books having small pages such as small Bibles, are often printed two hundred and fifty-six pages (one hundred and twenty-eight on each side at one time.

High grade, illustrated books are always printed on one side of the sheet at a time, the reverse side being printed after the first impression has dried properly. Thus a smooch, or "offset," the result of handling the paper before the ink has become dry, is prevented.

For convenience, I shall describe the process of printing a book from electrotype plates on a press which prints thirty-two pages at a time and on only one side of the paper.

Before ordering his paper, the publisher must first determine the size of the paper page of his proposed book, and from this arrive at the necessary size of the sheets of paper. He must also determine the thickness of the paper needed to give the finished book its proper bulk.

The quality of the paper and the size of the sheet being decided upon, and the number of pages known, any large paper house can tell the weight necessary to give the required thickness to the book.

On receipt of the printing order, with directions as to whether the book is to be trimmed or not, the printer first makes up what is called a "form" of so-called "patent" blocks on which the stereotype or electrotype plates are placed during the printing of the book. These blocks are made of metal planed to an even thickness of about three-fourths of an inch, so that when an electrotype plate is placed upon one, it will take only a few thicknesses of thin paper between it and the electrotyped page to make the whole "type-high," that is, as high as an ordinary piece of type.

These blocks are provided with catches, which project above the block and are turned over slightly, so as to receive the two beveled edges of the electrotype plate. The other two edges are provided with movable clamps, which are screwed tight against the flat edges of the electrotype plate by means of ratchets, thus holding the plate firmly in its place. It is necessary to know whether the binder is to fold the sheets by hand or by machine, and if the latter, what kind of machine, as different ones require different "imposition" or arrangement of pages. This being decided, the plates are fastened on the blocks so arranged that when the sheet is cut and folded the pages of the book will run consecutively. A typical form then appears like this:

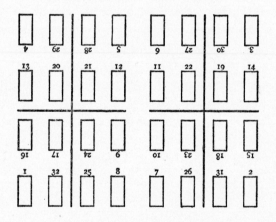

Notwithstanding the care that has been taken to have all the electrotype plates of even and uniform thickness, there is almost never a case where a form can be put on the press and printed off properly without considerable work being required to make the surface of the plates absolutely flat so that the entire printed part of the page will receive the same amount of ink and will press evenly on the paper.

The first step in making a press "ready" is to place a few sheets of paper around the cylinder. Over this a thick sheet of manila paper is shrunk, it being pasted under clamps on the front of the cylinder, and carried around and fastened to hooks on a rod on the back. The rod is then turned until the sheet is perfectly tight and smooth.

While the pressman is laying out his plates the feeder should be cutting thin sheets of paper the size of one of the plates. Some of these papers are cut about one inch shorter than the plates for "bevels," and these are pasted on the middle of the full-size pieces. These bevels and the larger "blank" sheets are to go between the plates and the blocks to overcome any variation there may be in the thickness and to make the surface of the form as nearly level as possible. The "bevels" raise the centers very slightly above the edges of the plate, thus reducing the pressure of the cylinder at the points of contact and departure, and saving the plates from wear.

The cylinder being properly packed, the form is fastened on the press so that the impression of the form will come in the middle of the paper sheets. Before leveling up the form with the bevels and blank sheets, the plates of all open or short pages, if any, are replaced with solid pages, as these sheets and underlay are to remain through the printing of all the forms of the book. The rollers are now put in the press and adjusted to just touch the inking table, the ink put on the rollers and distributed, and one impression printed on one of several sheets of thin paper which are run through the press together.[1] This printed sheet is then turned face down by the pressman and any unevenness of the impression noted. One of the printed pages is taken as a standard and by removing as many pieces of the thin sheets as necessary from under the plates where the impression is too heavy, and by adding where it is not heavy enough, the surface of the form is finally "evened," or made as nearly equal as possible.

After this another impression is taken, and of this sheet an "underlay" is made to further "even up" the form. The low places in the individual plates are carefully marked with crayon or a soft pencil on the impression, and the spots so marked are covered with a piece of thin paper. The printed pages are then cut out a little larger than the type page, and placed under the plates from which they were printed. The plates of the solid pages, which had been substituted for the open pages, are now removed, and the open pages are put back in their places on the form.

Up to this point, all the "making ready" which has

[1] If one sheet of paper were run through the press before "making ready," it would not receive any impression, there being a space equal to the thickness of ten sheets of paper between the cylinder and the surface of the type. A bunch of six or eight sheets is therefore run through to get an impression for "make-ready" purposes.

been done, is of permanent use in printing all of the forms of the book in question. The work that follows has to be done on each form as it is put on the press.

The pressman should have been getting "register." So that the headlines and the sides of the plates align properly, and that when both sides of the paper have been printed, the pages will exactly back each other, it is necessary to move plates to their exact position. The ink fountain should also have been so regulated by means of thumb-screws that the right amount of ink will run on the rollers and be distributed evenly over the form. Where too much ink shows on the printed sheet, the thumb-screws on the fountain are tightened a little, to decrease the flow, and where not enough ink shows the thumb-screws are loosened to increase its flow. This process is repeated until the "color" is all right. The grippers, which seize and carry the sheets of paper through the press, the reels, cylinder bands, and many other things have also to be adjusted. These cannot well be described, but have to be learned by actual experience.

The "making ready" and watching the sheets as they come from the press to see that the "color" does not vary, is the skillful part of the process. The feeding of the paper into the press is sometimes done by hand but is now done automatically by machines to a great extent.

While the press was being made ready, another set of men in charge of the paper have taken it out of the cases or bundles, counted out the number of sheets required for each form, piled it on hand trucks, keeping that required for each form separate, and have delivered it to the press. If a machine feeder is used, the paper is piled on the elevator of the feeder, from which it is automatically taken, one sheet at a time, and delivered on endless tapes to gauges on the feed board of the press, thus bringing every sheet in the same position each time. The number of sheets required for the order are printed from one form on one side and then from another form on the other side.

From the preceding it can be seen that to get a press ready may be a matter of hours, while, in the case of ordinary book work, a press generally prints from 1200 to 2000 impressions and more per hour.

The principal difference between making ready a form on a flat-bed perfecting press with two cylinders and on a single-cylinder press is in extra work necessary to obtain correct registering of the plates and in preventing an offset of the fresh ink on the second cylinder. Otherwise, a perfecting press is very much like two cylinder presses joined together. It has two sets of rollers, two ink fountains, two cylinders, two forms, etc., but only one feed board and one delivery. The sheet is fed to one cylinder and printed, taken from this cylinder by the second and printed on the second side, and delivered on the "flyboard" ready to go to the shipping department.

The process of making ready forms containing illustrations is practically the same as for plain ones, except that a new underlay is made for each form, and much more care and skill must be used on the cuts themselves. It frequently happens that one or even two days are spent making ready a form of half-tone cuts, before the actual printing, which takes perhaps half a day to do, can be begun.

In most offices, a special "cut overlay" is made for forms with cuts, or illustrations. The cut is placed on a hand press before the form is made up, and proofs on four different thicknesses of paper are made. The heaviest paper is used as a bottom sheet, and the others are pasted on it. Out of the next to the thickest paper of all, the solid blacks are cut and pasted accurately on the same places on the bottom sheet. From the second or next thinner sheet, the medium shades including the solid blacks are cut and pasted on the bottom sheet, thus building up the blacks and strong shadows. From the thinnest sheet of all, the high lights and very light shades are cut, and the rest of the sheet is pasted on the bottom one. In this way the solid blacks and dark shadows on the cut have three thicknesses on the overlay; the next shades two, and the light shades one, where the high lights are cut out altogether. This is the common form of "cut overlay" used in most offices; but there are many other kinds, notably the mechanical relief chalk overlay. These overlays are pasted on a light weight manila sheet which has previously been run through the press and on which an impression of the form has been made. Care must be taken that the overlays are super-imposed exactly over their corresponding impressions on the sheet.

This sheet is then pasted on the cylinder of the press

in such a position that it will be in perfect contact with the form. Over this sheet another layer or two of manila paper is placed, and finally a "top sheet" of heavier manila is tightly drawn around the cylinder, thus holding the overlays in a permanent position.

One of the great troubles which the printer has to contend with, is electricity in the paper. The pressman is unaware of its presence until he lifts a printed sheet from the pile and receives a slight shock, and finds the sheets stick together. In the case of a cut form, the ink is almost sure to be offset, and in printing the second side of the paper the feeder will have to stop frequently to separate the sheets. Much money has been spent and many devices originated to overcome this trouble. Ink manufacturers make a liquid preparation to be applied to the packing. A row of lighted gas-jets placed near the point where the sheet goes on to the "flyboard," a heated steam-pipe, and many other things have been used, but a device by which electricity is generated and carried into the press, and there neutralizing the electricity in the paper, is the best of them all.

The printed sheets are counted automatically by the press, and as fast as enough accumulate, they are piled on hand trucks and removed to the shipping room. Here they are "jogged up" so that the edges are even. If they are to be shipped away, they are tied up in bundles or nailed in cases and marked for shipment. If the bindery is connected with the pressroom, they are simply jogged, counted, and piled on trucks and delivered in this way.

THE PRINTING PRESS

By Frank J. Ball

PRINTING from movable type was, according to Professor Douglas, probably practiced in China as early as the Twelfth or Thirteenth Century, as there are Korean books printed from movable clay or wooden types in 1317.

The great discovery made by Gutenberg was that of forming every letter or character of the alphabet separately, so as to be capable of re-arrangement and forming in succession the pages of work, thereby avoiding the labor of cutting new blocks of types for every page.

The press used by Gutenberg and the early Dutch printers was a crude affair made of wood, having two upright timbers held together at the top and bottom by cross pieces of wood, and with two intermediate cross timbers. One of these intermediate cross timbers supported a wooden or stone "bed" on which the form of type was placed and through the other passed a large wooden screw, the lower point of which was attached to the center of a plate called the platen. The lower side of the platen was covered with a soft "packing" or blanket of cloth. After the type had been inked, a sheet of paper was laid on the form. The screw was then turned down until the platen firmly pressed the paper against the form and produced a printed sheet.

As a press so constructed had not the strength to impress the types firmly into the harsh and uneven hand-made paper, it was necessary to dampen the paper, making it more pliable and readily absorbing ink. This type of press was used without material change for 350 years.

Printing was brought to England in 1476 or 1477 by William Caxton. The first printing press set up in America was introduced by the Viceroy of Mexico, Antonio de Mendoza; and the first book printed in the New World was "The Ladder de St. Juan Climaco" (1536). The earliest press in the British-American colonies was brought over for Harvard College in 1635 and was set up by Stephen Daye. The "Bay Psalm Book" in 1640 was its first important work; but in 1639 it printed the "Freeman's Oath" and an almanac. In Philadelphia a press was set up in 1685; in New York in 1693.

The first improvement of the hand press was made about 1620 by William Janson Blauew of Amsterdam who employed a bed of stone on which the type rested which could be rolled in and out, making possible the inking of the type form without lifting it out by hand. The wooden screw was replaced by one made of iron and a new form of iron hand-lever for turning the screw.

The first decisive improvement of the printing press was made by the Earl of Stanhope in 1798. This press was entirely constructed of iron and while the iron impression screw was retained, it had connected to it a combination of levers whereby its power was greatly increased. Its greater strength made it possible to print larger forms and the use of harder packing resulted in sharper and clearer impression. Much less exertion was required to work the lever and at first printers accustomed to working on the old hand presses, found it difficult to work on the new one.

Many improvements speedily succeeded this press in most of which the screw was dismissed, the pressure being generally effected by levers, or by the simple and efficient principle of straightening a joint. Among those which met with great favor was the Columbian press invented by George Clymer of Philadelphia. This press was taken to England in 1818 and patented. The pressing power was produced by a long bar or handle acting on a combination of exceedingly powerful levers.

Samuel Rust of New York in 1827 patented an improved hand press known as the Washington press in which the hand-lever movement was reduced to its simplest and most powerful form. His patent was later purchased by R. Hoe & Co. who materially strengthened the press and sold more than seven thousand of such machines. They are still held in favor by photo engravers and some printers for taking fine proofs of photo-engraved plates, and taking proofs of book plates.

The improvements made on the hand press and the introduction of the cylinder press, did not materially add to production, although it was sorely needed, as the inking of the form done by the leather ink-balls was necessarily a slow operation. Books and newspapers printed in 1801 cannot be commended as better than those printed in 1501 as there had been no improvement in types and but few changes in the old methods of printing. The hand press improved by Blauew of Amsterdam was left by him about as slow as it was in the days of Caxton and Aldus. Its frame and platen were of wood and its bed rest was of stone. One pressman inked the type with a pair of leather balls and was followed by another who pulled the bar. By hard labor the press was able to produce seven hundred sheets printed on both sides in ten hours. When the workman was an expert and loved his work and had been provided with good materials and allowed time for its accomplishment, his workmanship was excellent but these conditions seldom were combined.

The Earl of Stanhope and Frederick Koenig tried without success to find a substitute for the ink-balls. Faster printing machinery would have been impractical without cylindrical inking rollers made of glue and molasses, a material which had been used in the Staffordshire potteries for many years. Its adaptability for receiving and imparting ink or color was perceived by an unknown English printer, who induced the makers of cylinder presses to try the novel compound, as rollers of leather, cloth or silk were found ineffective. Without the swift-moving composition roller there could be no proper inking of type on fast machines. It was the slow, dabbing move-

ment of the inking ball that made Koenig fail in all
attempts to quicken the hand press or his first cylinder
press.

Another contribution to the development of book
printing was the art of stereotyping invented by the Earl
of Stanhope about 1804. Under the old conditions, a
publisher did not dare to print a large number of copies
of a book unless he believed it would have a quick sale.
Books were bulky and took up too much space, consequently the types for a first edition were distributed
when they left the press; they had to be re-set with renewed chances of error in the second edition. Re-set-
ting for two or more editions added largely to the cost
of the book and limited its supply. The process first
used, known as the plaster process, served book printers
for types for about fifty years, but failed for engravings.

The practice of the art was brought to New York
by David Bruce in 1813 and the first book stereotyped
was the "Westminster Catechism" made by J. Watts
and Company in June of the same year. The papier-
mâché process of stereotyping, by which a mould of the
type is made on prepared paper, was invented by Genoux
of France. The process was made practicable on rotary
presses by Charles Craske, a New York electrotyper, in
1863, by the invention of a curved casting box, making
it possible to produce quickly, plates of newspaper pages
which fitted perfectly on the cylinders of rotary presses.
While the first curved stereotype plate was made for

use on the Hoe type revolving newspaper presses having four, six, eight and ten impression cylinders, it met with no favor on such machines. Its success was made possible by the invention by William Bullock in 1865 of a rotary printing machine which printed a large newspaper on both sides of a continuous web of paper and delivered 10,000 unfolded copies in an hour. The stereotype plate with the papier-mâché matrix is still in use in all newspaper establishments.

The history of the printing press is a history of evolution; when early in the Nineteenth Century printing had then been done for three hundred and fifty years without material improvement of the printing press, the demand for more and cheaper books and newspapers became so imperative that many inventors entered seriously into the business of improving the printing press. In 1804 Frederick Koenig of Saxony went to London with the model of an improved platen press intended to be self-inking and to more than double the production of the old hand press. After many years of experiment he had to abandon all efforts to improve the old method of printing from two flat surfaces, but he was entirely successful in his method of printing upon a flat surface from a rotating cylinder. The machine so constructed was fairly tested on a book form in 1811 but was found unsatisfactory for book printing and was placed in the office of the London *Times*. This machine, although crude and imperfect, proved a turning point in printing,

First Cylinder Printing Press Installed in America

Modern Two-revolution Cylinder Press

for it demonstrated the greater speed and merit of the cylinder movement.

The cylinder of this press had three impression surfaces with spaces between them, and each covered with a soft blanket. With each forward movement of the type-bed the cylinder made one-third of a revolution and then came to a standstill, while the bed returned to its starting point. The spaces between the impression surfaces allowed the type form to pass under the cylinder without touching the blankets. At the end of the cylinder and at equal distances along its circumference, were hinged the frisket frames, each fitted with tapes having reel springs at one end. The frisket frame of the uppermost impression surface rested in a vertically inclined position against the high framework of the inking mechanism. The sheet of paper was placed upon the blanket and the cylinder then turned forward, drawing the frisket frame down with it, while the tapes kept taut by the reel springs, adjusted themselves to the curvature of the cylinder and held the sheet upon it. After one-third of a revolution, the cylinder came to a stop to let the type-bed return. On the next forward movement of the bed and the next one-third revolution of the cylinder, the impression was made and on the next repetition of these movements, the sheet was taken off by hand and the cylinder returned to its original position to have another sheet placed on the first frisket. At every complete revolution of the cylinder and three complete reciprocating movements of the bed, three sheets were printed. The inking mechanism was similar to that employed on the bed and platen press. The inking rollers were covered with leather, having the unavoidable seam, and the difficulty of keeping the leather rollers in condition, gave less uniform inking of the form than could be had with the hand balls.

While Koenig's press was faster than the hand press, its many shortcomings forced book printers to reject it, but John Walter, proprietor of the London *Times*, lent aid and encouragement to Koenig and in 1814 two cylinder presses were in daily use on the London *Times*. Koenig had been materially helped in his experiments by his countryman, Adreas Bauer, and many Englishmen who developed his imperfect plans, of whom Bensley, Napier and Applegath deserve notice. In Koenig's bed movement, the driving gear on the end of a rising and falling shaft ran on top of a rack attached to the bottom of the bed in order to drive the bed in one direction, and then descending around the end of the rack ran in the bottom side of the same rack to drive the bed in the opposite direction, and ascending at the other end to repeat the movement. This bed movement was improved by D. Napier, a London machinist and is still employed by some press makers at the present time.

A few years later, Applegath and Cowper greatly simplified the cylinder press and were first to invent the iron ink plate attached to the type bed. The distributing rollers were placed at an angle across the ink table and introduced the roller and scraping blade in the ink fountain. These improvements enabled the rollers, then made of glue and molasses, to distribute the ink more evenly than before.

More important, however, was Napier's invention about 1824, of grippers which seized the sheet of paper at its front edge and drew it from the feed board while the cylinder was in motion, and of a method of alternately depressing and raising the impression cylinders on the forward and backward stroke of the type-bed, making it unnecessary to have a part of the cylinders of smaller diameter than the rest to allow the type to pass under it as the bed returned. Cylinders of smaller diameter were used, the cylinder making three revolutions to one forward and backward stroke of the bed. These presses were found satisfactory for newspaper printing, but owing to mechanical imperfections were not fitted for a good grade of book printing. The invention of the grippers, the inking table, improved bed movement and composition rollers, greatly improved the printing qualities of the press, and added to its production. It was yet necessary for a second operator to take the sheet from the tapes and place it on the delivery table. This mechanical device called the fly, patented by Isaac Adams about 1845, was used on the Adams press and on the fast-running single and double cylinder newspaper presses. It was not generally used on cylinder, book and job presses from which printed sheets were taken off by fly boys as late as 1860.

Though important improvements in printing machinery were first made in England, English machines as well as those of other European countries have never been popular in the United States. The production of the American builders of presses and founders of type are preferred at higher prices, because they have been made to meet the exacting requirements. Many of the American inventions are based on new principles. After Koenig's failure to make a faster hand press, foreign inventors gave up the platen movement as impractical, but Isaac Adams of Boston took it up from a new point of departure and made it successful.

In 1827 he constructed the machine known as the Adams power press. At first it was a crude affair and turned by a hand wheel with a frame of wood, and fitted to print forms of small size, but it was afterward made of iron entirely and improved so that it could print a sheet on one side only of 30 x 40 inches at the rate of eight hundred sheets per hour. Considering the larger form printed, as well as its greater speed, the Adams press did in one day the work of ten hand presses quite as well as it had been done before, and its provisions for inking and exact register were of the best. For more than fifty years the Adams press was preferred for book printing. It still has friends, the University Press of Cambridge having a number of such presses in daily operation. As late as 1882 Theodore L. DeVinne bought from R. Hoe & Co. two Adams presses for the printing of small editions of books for which they were well adapted. These were the last Adams presses made. They were sold in 1905 to a Boston book printer and are still in active use.

The introduction of the improved Adams press came about 1838–1840. In 1835 all of Harper & Brothers books were printed on hand presses. As late as 1849 the firm of Banks & Gould printed all its books on the hand press, but this was the last attempt in New York City to employ it for commercial book work.

The first cylinder press made in America was bought by Van Benthuysen & Sons of Albany, N. Y., about 1828–1830. It was presumably made by R. Hoe & Co. This press was used for the printing of the *Temperance Recorder*.

The New York *Sun,* established in 1832, was printed on the hand press.

Two or three men working strenuously in reliefs of fifteen minutes were able to print about five hundred sheets in an hour. While the cylinder presses were improved and were found indispensable in the printing of newspapers, book printers did not find them adaptable for the printing of books. The cylinder presses made up to 1860 were of weak construction and wore types badly and were particularly destructive to stereotype plates which were largely used before the introduction of electrotype plates. Pressmen called them type smashers and those of the earlier models fairly deserved the name. The American Bible Society tried to utilize the cylinder press for printing Bibles but found them too destructive to type. So deep rooted was this prejudice against cylinder presses that as late as 1890 publishers owning book plates would stipulate that the printing must be done on Adams presses. The publisher of the "History of Brooklyn," in four volumes, printed in 1869 and illustrated with many wood engravings, had the printing of the wood engravings done by John Mooney on hand presses. The text was done in eight-page forms on Adams presses. As late as 1886 two concerns in New York City having hand presses only, still found profitable employment in the printing of wood engravings for book publishers.

In 1872 J. G. Holland and Roswell Smith decided on the publication of *Scribner's Magazine* (afterward *The Century*), which from a literary and artistic standpoint was designed to far surpass *Harper's Monthly Magazine*, then considered the best printed magazine in America. As John F. Trow had the largest and best equipped book printing plant in New York City, the printing of the magazine was given to them. Their equipment consisted of about thirty Adams presses with four or five cylinders.

The Adams presses failed to meet the exacting requirements set by the publishers as it was found necessary that the paper be dampened and made pliable before printing. As an aid to good impression, a felt or rubber blanket with six or eight soft sheets was used for the impression surfaces. When types only were printed, the dampened paper and elastic impression made strong and easily readable print, but this method which was good for types, was bad for woodcuts in which shallow engraving was unavoidable. Elastic impression pressed surplus ink in the counters or depressions of the engravings, and seriously damaged the contrasts of light and shade made by the engraver.

Two other printers tried to print the magazine on Adams presses and in 1876 Theodore L. DeVinne who had demonstrated that it was possible to print by cylinder presses, type and sharp lines clearly on calendered paper without moistening it, was asked to undertake the printing of *Scribner's Magazine*. When it was learned that he intended to do this work on stop-cylinder presses, rival publishers and printers predicted failure.

While the first numbers printed on stop-cylinder presses were typographically good, it was not all smooth sailing. There were no pressmen who possessed sufficient skill to make ready or prepare for printing a woodcut as sharp and clear as it could be done on a hand press. This problem was solved by engaging the best hand pressmen in New York City, from whom the younger men learned the art of printing woodcuts. As the printing was done against a smooth hard pressboard which had not the resiliency of a felt or rubber blanket, the greatest care was required in the adjustment of the impression on the type and woodcuts. Four days often were required in the make-ready of a sixteen page magazine form before printing could be done. Seven thousand sheets printed on one side in a ten hour work day, was considered satisfactory. While the production was much greater than could be had on the Adams press, the stronger and faster presses of today, together with better appliances and greater skill of the pressmen, has cut down the make-ready time and greatly increased production.

The publication of books in the middle of the last century, was all done in the cities of Boston, New York and Philadelphia, and there were located in these cities many printing establishments having from five to forty Adams presses. The possibility of printing large editions of magazine forms without wear of plates on cylinder presses, brought about the gradual displacement of the Adams press, together with the wetting machines, drying rooms, and hydraulic presses used for smoothing the finished sheets. The Adams press was not without friends, however, as many book critics contended that the moist paper, soft packing, and greater indentation of the types into the paper, tend to slightly thicken the types, making the page more readable, and adding to the comfort of men who have to wear spectacles. The strong and perfectly adjusted cylinder press does not thicken sharp lines and under the conditions that control ordinary presswork, it is not possible to show vivid blackness on thin lines that will not hold the needed ink.

Excess of ink will not always give the desired blackness. Weak types make weak presswork. Experienced book makers avoid thin faced types and select types of heavy face which will hold the needed ink. The strongly built and correctly designed cylinder press of today produces book printing with greater strength and clearness than ever produced on the Adams press.

About 1828–1830 R. Hoe & Co. of New York who had been making hand presses since 1822 began the building of flat bed cylinder presses. While their first press, the single, large, or drum cylinder press possessed but little merit, they soon took the lead in the improvement of the cylinder press.

The drum cylinder press was soon followed by a three revolution small cylinder press, modeled after the Napier press which could produce from 1500 to 1800 sheets per hour, printed on one side. This was soon followed by the double cylinder press having one type-bed and two impression cylinders which was capable of producing with two feeders 3500 sheets per hour on one side.

The New York *Sun* during the Civil War, used two of these machines. The product of this press was too small for any paper with increasing circulation, forms had to go to press early, to the shutting out of news, and finish late, to the annoyance of subscribers.

A notable attempt to increase production was made by R. Hoe & Co., in the invention of a rotary press, which turned out four papers printed on one side at every revolution of the central cylinder, which contained the type. Machines having six, eight and ten cylinders were afterward made. The column rules were fitted into a section of the cylinder between which the movable types were fastened. It was not possible to use large types. These machines were very popular and were used by the leading newspapers of America, and found their way to London and Paris.

In the first World Fair held in London in 1850 Thomas Nelson of Edinburgh exhibited a little cylinder printing machine, which printed at one operation from an endless roll of paper, a small hand bill on both sides.

The possibility of a larger machine was not appreciated by European press builders, but the principle was successfully utilized by William Bullock who in 1865 was the first to make a machine which printed a large newspaper successfully on both sides of a continuous web of paper. This machine enabled the newspaper publisher to print 10,000 copies within an hour, without the assistance of feeders.

R. Hoe & Company, who recognized that the Bullock press was a serious competitor of the type revolving press, brought out in 1871 an improved rotary, known as the web press, which printed from curved stereotyped plates, 10,000 to 12,000 copies in an hour, and piled the printed copies, counted, folded and ready for delivery. The great need for increased speed has led press builders to improve and simplify the folding mechanism which limited the speed of the press to the extent that it is possible to print on an octuple press 96,000 16-page newspapers in an hour. Such large newspaper machines find their way to many foreign countries and are made by R. Hoe & Co., Goss Co. of Chicago, Scott & Duplex Co.

In 1885 the circulation of illustrated magazines had increased so largely that it was impracticable to print them properly, and on time, on any form flat bed cylinder press. A new form of web press was made by R. Hoe & Co., for the advertising forms and plain forms of the *Century Magazine* which printed them from curved electrotype plates in forms of 64 pages, and delivered folded, four signatures of 16 pages each, in an entirely satisfactory manner and performed the work of ten cylinder presses. The success of this machine led C. B. Cottrell & Co., to soon follow with a rotary press for magazine printing, which delivered the sheets flat, without folding. This type of machine is much used by magazine printers on forms having full color.

From 1830 to 1865 but few important improvements were made on the cylinder press—printing up to that time was at a low ebb. The Adams press met fully all demands for book printing; the drum cylinder press when operated by a competent workman, answered fairly well on such jobbing and catalog work as could be had.

The close of the Civil War and the rapid growth of our inland cities, brought about a demand for more and better printing. Important improvements were made by R. Hoe & Co., C. B. Cottrell & Co., and C. Potter, Jr. & Co., who employed the Napier movement.

Andrew Campbell about 1870 brought out a two revolution press, and was the first American inventor to discard the Napier bed movement and used the Henry or Middleton movement, which came into use about

1850. This press was highly favored by printers. The design was good but the weak construction of the bed movement and the faulty mechanism for retarding the bed at the end of the stroke, brought about injury to the press when slight over-speeding was done.

Campbell was an ingenious mechanic, and also a prolific inventor; instead of strengthening the weakness of a good design, he brought out something entirely different, necessitating making new patterns and discarding expensive machine tools.

The stop-cylinder type of machine was brought out by Dutartre, France, in 1852, and in 1860 by William Dawson and David Otley, Wharfedale, York, England. In 1870 R. Hoe & Co. brought out an improved press of this type. Its greater strength, perfect register and fine ink distribution led printers to hail it as having all the qualifications of a perfect printing press. In the smaller sizes, the stop-cylinder press was capable of fairly good speed, but in the larger sizes the mechanism which brought the heavy cylinder to a full stop after every revolution proved inadequate, curtailing production. The stop-cylinder press held its friends for thirty years or more.

The printing houses of thirty years ago nearly all had stop-cylinder presses for the finest printing and two revolution presses for work on which greater production was required. The introduction of coated paper and the half-tone illustrations made it difficult to deliver without smutting a printed sheet which had to pass over a rear delivery cylinder, over strings, and laid on the delivery board by the fly.

Andrew Campbell had adopted the front fly delivery on his two revolution presses in 1870 on which the fly engaged the unprinted side of the sheet and laid it on the delivery board printed side down. This type of delivery did not obtain full popularity as many printers demanded a press which delivered printed side up, enabling the pressman to watch the work as it comes from the press.

The improved two revolution presses of 1876 were capable of good speed, but were weak on the impression and were found wanting on close register work and easily got out of adjustment.

In 1889 Robert Miehle, a Chicago pressman who had studied the operation of the two revolution press and was fully aware of it shortcomings, invented a simple and powerful bed movement, which drives the type bed in perfect unison with the cylinder. Miehle accomplished this by placing on the hanger on the lower side of the bed and attaching two racks facing each other, one line of teeth being above, the other below, the gear wheel fixed on a horizontal shaft moving from the line above to the line below, alternately driving the bed forward and backward.

On the gear wheel is a large roller which after each stroke is completed falls behind a straight cam, or slide; the toothed wheel drops out of the rack and the type bed is then actuated by a veritable crank motion, which graduates its speed, carries it over its center, accelerates it again and drops it into mesh with the lower rack, to give the bed the next movement.

The great strength and precision of this movement makes it possible to drive the bed at a high speed and reverse it without shock or vibration.

Miehle's fame does not rest entirely on his invention of the bed movement. He gave his attention to every function or movement of the press, the ink fountain was made stronger and more positive as to fine adjustment, distributing rollers are driven by a positive device insuring better ink distribution; form roller adjustments underwent improvements. The changes made on the feed guides, grippers, gripper tumbler and the graduated raise of the cylinder, tended very much to insure perfect register. The dual delivery, making it possible to deliver a sheet printed side up or printed side down is of great importance to printers.

Most important was his strengthening of the cylinder and type-bed, using four tracks in which the bed traveled for the smaller sizes and six tracks for large sizes, together with powerful supports for the bed. It was found to possess all the good qualities of the stop-cylinder press and its high rate of speed and ease of handling made it very popular in this and other countries.

Up to 1887 printing press inventors had failed to properly appreciate the pressure required to impress the types on only a narrow line of the printing surface of a

cylinder press, the weakness of the press when printing
a heavy form caused spring of the cylinder, and spring
of the bed, which necessitated the use of extra packing.
On a platen press it matters not at all whether more or
less sheets are on the packing, but on a cylinder the over-
packing or underpacking causes the face of the cylinder
to move faster or slower than the bed bringing about
wear to the types; nor is the perfectly designed cylinder
rotary press of today incapable of wearing types, in the
hands of an incompetent workman, or if slightly out of
adjustment the presses of today are fully as destructive
to types as were the weak, poorly constructed machines
of fifty years ago.

The possibility of printing 200,000 impressions or
more without perceptible wear of plates on cylinder and
on rotary presses is an evidence that the skill of pressmen trained during the last thirty years has kept pace
fully with the genius of the inventor.

The flat-bed perfecting press having a double type-
bed, an ink table, fountain and inking rollers at each end
of the bed, and two cylinders, the sheet is fed to the first
cylinder and after printing transferred to and completed
on the second cylinder, was first invented in 1824; revived in 1850 and again brought out in 1880. Three
firms engaged in their manufacture, and they enjoyed
a certain degree of popularity, but their faulty design
soon made them troublesome and unfitted them for good
book printing and the slow speed made them unprofitable
on cheap work.

The present type of improved perfecting press now used by many book printers was brought out in 1901. While a satisfactory market was found for them in England and other European countries, American book printers having in mind the troubles developed on the earlier presses, were skeptical as to the economy of such machines.

In 1915 the shortage of labor and increased costs led several printers to increase production by installing perfecting presses. This experiment proved highly successful and perfecting presses are now used in all large book printing houses. The objectionable "offset" or smutting of the sheet first printed on the packing of the second cylinder which prints the reverse side of the sheet is overcome by the employment of an oil fountain and plush rollers which cover a thin film of volatile oil on the packing of the second impression cylinder, and the use of a top sheet of specially prepared paper, which has ink refusing properties.

The perfect register which can be had on the perfecting press makes it specially adaptable for the printing of bible paper or tender stock which may be difficult to register on single presses. The presses are made of a size capable of printing on both sides 128 pages of a book form on a sheet 45 x 68 inches. Automatic feeding machines on which a host of inventors have devoted forty years of improvement and are as nearly perfect as human ingenuity can make them, are generally used on perfecting and single presses, together with an automatic piling device capable of holding from 6000 to 10,000 sheets perfectly straightened.

The practical speed of a large perfecting press is 1600 per hour, and while large editions are preferred, book printers find them profitable on editions of 2500 copies.

The mechanical principles of the rotary press are in fact simpler than those of the flat-bed cylinder press, which has been brought to such a point of development that no more improvements as to speed appear possible. When forty years ago the rotary press had demonstrated the possibility of printing magazines in large editions with greater economy, it was thought that the rotary press would supplant flat-bed presses in the printing of books. As books are seldom printed in editions larger than 50,000 and editions of 250 are not uncommon, it is found that the length of time required in preparing the form for printing the various sizes of pages and the difficulty of obtaining the proper paper in roll form were obstacles impossible to overcome on rotary presses.

During three hundred years of printing, each generation of printers followed more or less faithfully in the path made by their predecessors. The improvement made in the cylinder press made it possible to print types and wood engravings with greater sharpness, tending toward a greater delicacy of print. This weak style of printing reached its highest development in 1880, then came the reaction. Book publishers demanded new type faces having greater blackness. DeVinne, who had been so strong an advocate of printing in sharp, clear lines, changed with the times, and in 1882 bought an Adams press for the printing of fine books of limited editions. His first book, printed for the Grolier Club in 1884, "A Decree of Star Chamber," was a small octavo volume of eighty pages with an introduction of six pages, printed on dampened, hand made paper. The price of two dollars per copy was thought high for so small a book by some members of the club, yet twenty years afterward a copy of this book sold for $225.00.

PRINTING INK

By James A. Ullman

MAKING printing ink consists of grinding a black, white or colored pigment, into a suitable varnish. The pigment is that element which makes the impression visible, while the varnish is the vehicle—firstly, carrying the pigment during the grinding operation, and secondly, during its distribution on the press to the type, from the type to the paper; and thirdly, binding it to the paper.

A complete printing ink factory, therefore, consists of three distinct plants, one for the production of varnishes, the second for the manufacture of pigments, and the third for the grinding of pigments in the varnishes.

Speaking generally, varnishes are divided into three classes, the first and second of which are varnishes proper, i.e., resin and linseed varnishes, while the third class consists of dryers and other agents whose purpose is to influence the drying and consistency of inks.

Referring to the varnishes proper, these are produced by the destructive distillation of resin in huge cast-iron stills. By this process the solid resin or colophony is split up into water, various resinic acids or naphthas, and resin oils of various specific gravities and consistencies, all of which are separated from each other into separate containers ready to receive them. As one distillation is not sufficient to purify the resin oils from the water and acid, which not only give the resulting ink an obnoxious odor but is injurious to type, plates, etc., the distillation is repeated a number of times until the oils are thoroughly neutralized or purified. The grades of varnishes made from these resin oils are used for the cheaper classes of printing inks, not only because of their lower cost, but because they are more suitable for the class of work for which such inks are used.

The linseed varnishes are made by boiling refined linseed oils at a very high temperature. The linseed oil loses its acrid elements by volatilization and gradually becomes thick and viscous, the various "numbers" or consistencies of these varnishes being dependent upon the length of time during which the oil is subjected to the process and the temperature.

The dryers are produced by adding to the linseed oil, during the process of boiling, suitable oxidizing agents, such as compounds of lead or manganese, by means of which the oil is chemically affected, i.e., oxidized. Such dryers when added to printing ink, attract the oxygen of the air, transferring it by catalytic action to the varnish of the ink, thus causing it to oxidize more rapidly, or to become, as it is commonly called, dry.

We now come to the manufacture of pigments. This covers such a wide range that it can only be briefly touched upon within the limits of a short article. Pigments are of many kinds and classes. Blacks alone would form a large chapter by themselves, yet all of them consist of carbon produced by the combustion of hydrocarbons of various kinds, and according to their origin they are the so-called carbon blacks, lamp blacks, spirit blacks, oil blacks, Frankfort blacks, etc., each of which has its distinct and peculiar properties and value for its specific purpose.

The other pigments fall naturally into two divisions, —chemical colors and the so-called "lakes." The chemical colors are in general of mineral origin, produced by the action of one chemical upon the other, or in some cases by physical or chemical action upon earths and ores. In the first group, we have such colors as vermilions, white lead, chrome yellows, the ferrocyanide blues (Milori blues, bronze blues, Prussian blues, Chinese blues, Antwerp blues, Paris blues, Berlin blues), ultramarines, etc.; in the second group, such colors as cyanides, umbers, Indian red, and many others.

The lakes are principally formed by the use of coaltar derivatives,—usually incorrectly grouped as anilines. These are produced by precipitating water-soluble dyes upon a suitable substratum or base. Their shades, strength, brilliancy, permanency, and working qualities are dependent upon the nature of the dye itself, upon the nature or percentage of substratum or base, and also upon the precipitating agents. This class of colors is today by far the most important of all, since through great progress made in chemistry in recent years, it is possible to make them of the greatest strength and permanency, together with a brilliance of shade heretofore impossible to attain.

Having disposed of the products which are the principal raw materials of printing ink, we now come to the ink itself. Being provided with all the varnishes, pigments, dryers, etc., of suitable qualities and shades, it is necessary to combine them in the correct proportions, after selecting such as will be mutually compatible, and to grind them to the utmost fineness. The machinery necessary consists, first, of mixers in which the ingredients are thoroughly incorporated with each other. This being done, the resultant mixture or pulp, as it is called, is ground upon mills formed of rollers or cylinders, which are set in close contact by means of screws and made to revolve by power. Between these rollers the pulp is passed again and again, the number of times dependent upon the consistency of the ink and the nature of the pigment, until it is ground or comminuted to the utmost fineness. The result is printing ink as it is known to the printer, varying in consistency, strength, intensity, permanency, brilliancy, drying, and other working qualities, according to the nature of the various varnishes, dryers and pigments with which it is made.

PRINTER'S ROLLER

By Albert S. Burlingham

NOTWITHSTANDING the fact that no one thing connected with the art of printing had done more toward the advancement of that art than the simple inking appliance familiarly and commonly known as "the printer's roller,"—without which, indeed, the evolution of the power printing press from the primitive hand machines of the fathers would not have been possible,—it is an inexplicable truth that historians and encyclopædia makers who have made investigation of the origin and progress of the art seem to have attached so little of importance to the invention or introduction of the composition roller that only meager and casual reference is made to it. Even its predecessor, the "inkball," receives but scant courtesy at the hands of these chroniclers, for while they enter into the minutest detail (and properly so) in investigating as to whom the world is indebted for the idea of movable types and the invention of the printing press, they have not thought it worth their while to rescue from oblivion the suggester or adapter or constructor—whatever he may have been—of the device by which those types were inked to receive the impression from that press, and without which neither types nor press would have been of any avail.

It seems to be established beyond doubt, however, that the first suggestion of a roller to take the place of the ink-balls in applying ink to type forms was that of William Nicholson, with whom, also, the idea of the cylinder press originated, in 1790. He recognized the fact that no power press on the cylinder principle could be of practical use without an inking apparatus different from the primitive ink-balls. These were hollowed-out blocks of beech, mounted with a handle, the cavity stuffed with wool and covered with untanned sheepskin which had been well trodden until it was soft and pliable.

The early printing presses were made of wood, and two men were required to work a press—one to make the impressions and one to ink the forms with the balls. The ink was contained in a receptacle called the ink-table. It was enclosed on three sides, and was attached firmly to one post, or cheek, of the press, on which were the racks for holding the ink-balls when not in use. A beechen implement, resembling somewhat our potato masher, and called the "brayer," was used to manipulate the ink as it lay on the table; an iron shovel, known as the "slicer," being used to portion out from the mass of ink such quantities as were needed from time to time for the brayer.

It required much strength to manipulate the ink-balls properly, and thus it was a man's work. Taking up ink with them from the table, the operator vigorously beat the balls together with a rolling movement, turning them a little at a time so as to make the ink cover the entire surface and distribute it perfectly thereon. Then the type-forms were beaten with them until they were properly inked. The work of printing off an edition was divided between the two men, one manipulating the ink-balls for an hour, and then taking his turn at the press, while for the next hour his fellow-workman attended to the inking.

William Nicholson, seeing at once that the idea of a cylinder press could never be worked out to practical perfection with such a process of inking as that, built up an inking roller with manifold layers of cloth, which he covered with the trodden sheep-pelt surface used in the ink-balls, the distribution of the ink on the roller to be made by contact with a revolving cylinder of wood. The idea was there, but that it would have had the intended result was never known, for although Nicholson's press contained nearly all the principles on which the cylinder presses of our day are constructed, it lacked one vital feature—the attaching of the type-forms to the cylinders—and was consequently not of any practical use.

The Earl of Stanhope, who, in 1798, invented the first iron frame and "platen" press, with the improvement of levers in addition to screws to give the impression, coupled with his object Nicholson's idea of an inking roller or revolving cylinder. He spent large sums in trying to find a substance that he could utilize for that purpose. He investigated with the skins of many animals, domestic and wild, and tanned and dressed in various ways. Different textures of cloth and varieties of silk were used, but without success. The seam that was necessary down the entire length of the roller was one great impediment to success, and even if that could have been overcome, the proper softness and pliability of surface for receiving and depositing the ink evenly and smoothly on the type could not be obtained from any of the processes experimented with; and Stanhope's improvement in printing presses was still subject to the inconvenience of the ancient ink-balls.

In 1807 a printer named Maxwell made a sheep-skin roller which he introduced into Philadelphia. It failed of success, and the printers returned to the ink-balls. This Maxwell roller was reintroduced by Fanshaw, a New York printer, in 1815, but the printers of that city rejected it.

The inventors in England were still busily engaged in trying to solve the problem of the cylinder press that Nicholson had more than suggested in 1790, and the one great obstacle to success was the absence of a proper substance for supplying the need of an inking roller, the difficulty of the type and cylinder having been overcome by the invention of the "turtle" form. In 1813 a man whose name one historian gives as B. Foster, another as T. B. Foster, and to whom another refers as "Forster, an ingenious printer, employed by S. Hamilton, at Weymouth, England," one day visited the Staffordshire pottery. In a coloring process in use there Forster, or Foster, noticed a peculiar composition that covered the surface of the potter's "dabber." It was moist, pliable, and elastic. The historians do not say so, but we may well imagine that this "ingenious printer," seeing in that composition what he believed to be the long-sought substance that would do away with the sheep pelt as an inking device, with all that implied to the progress of the art of printing, must have awaited with feelings of acute anxiety the answer of the potter to his query as to what that composition was.

And what was it? "Glue and treacle,"—two of the simplest of articles, and the easiest to obtain. The printer experimented with them, and although he was the first to put to practical use in the art of printing the thing that revolutionized it and advanced it to its present state of wonderful perfection, yet so far as the printed chronicle of him goes, we do not know what his Christian name was, or whether his surname was Foster or Forster; and one chronicler states that it was in 1813, and another that it was in 1815, that he discovered roller composition to his fellow-printers.

The collateral evidence, however, is to the effect that it was in 1813. Forster (admitting that to have been his name), proved the availability of glue and molasses as an inking surface, not by using it in the form of a roller, but by coating a canvas with it, and using the canvas thus prepared in place of the sheep pelt on inking balls. From this the press inventors got the idea of coating a wooden cylinder with the composition. Applegath & Cowper, inventors of the Applegath cylinder press, were the first to adapt it in roller form, and for a time held a patent on the use of it; but the courts of England decided that there could be no patent on the composition, and substitutes for the manufacture of rollers having been devised which were no infringement on Applegath & Cowper's moulds, the compound came into open use, and Koenig, who had so improved and perfected Nicholson's ideas and plans for a power cylinder press, was able, in 1814, by the adaptation of the glue and molasses roller, to print the first edition of a newspaper that was ever run from a cylinder press— the historic edition of the London *Times*. The problem of the inking apparatus solved, there was no longer any limit to the exercise of inventive genius in the advancement of the printing art; and it is, therefore, to the printer's roller, more than to any one thing, that that art owes its wonderful preëminence today.

There is no record in any of the histories of printing, or in encyclopædias, of who it was that introduced the composition roller into use in this country, or any reference to the date when it came into service. De Vinne, in his *Typographia*, published in 1876, says that ink-balls were in use here "fifty years ago," or in 1826; but it must have been only in isolated and out-of-the-way rural printing offices, for it can hardly be supposed that Yankee "go-aheadativeness" would have failed to recognize at once the importance of the discovery, or have long delayed its general adoption, although the hand press, with many improvements, remained the universal printing machine in the United States until 1822, when the Treadwell power press gave the first impulse to more rapid printing. The Treadwell was not a cylinder press, but its invention would have been of no consequence without the composition roller.

It is certain, however, that more than sixty years ago the melting pot and roller mould had become an important adjunct to every rural printing office, and the making of a new roller was an event in the routine of the establishment. The orthodox mixture for the composition in the printing office where the writer of this was the "devil" forty-seven years ago, was "a pint of sugar-house molasses to every pound of the best glue, with a tablespoonful of tar to every three pints and three pounds." And that was the customary composition of that day among country printers.

There is a tradition among printers and roller-makers that the first roller turned out in this country was moulded in a stove pipe; but whether it was or not, and no matter who the first roller-maker might have been, it is a fact that the advance in the art of roller-making has had to be rapid in order to keep pace with the vast improvements in the cylinder press which the first composition called into use, and the old-fashioned glue and molasses rollers would be now of no more service to them than would the primitive ink-balls which the roller replaced. A comparison between the mode of making a roller in the early days of the business and the methods in use today will be of interest.

In the old days the composition was cooked in a caldron over a coal fire, with water between two jackets to make the steam that forced the melting. The cast-iron moulds were placed near a stove to give them the necessary warmth of inner surface, a warm mould being required to give a good "face" to the roller in the casting. While cooking, the composition was constantly stirred with a stick to assist in the proper assimilation of the ingredients. After it had reached the proper stage, it was strained from the melting kettle into pouring kettles, similar to ordinary milk pails. The composition was poured from the top. Naturally, this let into the moulds, with the composition, the air bubbles and froth that were always present, which caused imperfections in the rollers. After pouring, it was necessary to let the moulds stand all night, so the composition might become sufficiently cool to permit the "drawing" of the rollers. This was effected by placing a stick against the iron journal at one end of the roller core and pushing until the roller was forced out of the mould.

But the roller factory of today is quite a different affair. Instead of separate moulds standing about a stove to get ready for the pouring, there are moulds in nests, or cylinders, resembling a Gatling gun, or a tubular boiler. There will perhaps be twenty roller moulds in a nest. The cylinders are balanced in the center on journals, thus enabling the workman to place them at any angle desired, for purposes of oiling the moulds and loading them with the roller cores. The cylinders have hot and cold water contact, by which they may be surrounded by either at will. To warm the moulds the cylinder is put in an upright position, and hot water circulated about it the required length of time.

The composition—which is something more than the old-time glue and molasses—is prepared for pouring by melting in a double-jacketed steam kettle, the stirring being done by a mixer run by steam power. When ready, the composition is drawn off from the bottom of the cooking kettles into pouring kettles which have air-tight hoods. To these a hose is attached, the other end of the hose being connected with a tank which is charged with air by a pump. The hose being then attached to the cylinder, the air is introduced from the tank into the pouring kettle, forcing the composition upward into the cylinder, and all air from the moulds. This insures a perfect roller.

When the composition has reached the top of the roller stocks, the valve at the bottom of the cylinder is closed, and the process is continued to the next cylinder ready for pouring. The cooling of the cylinders is effected by turning the cold water current around them, and a nest of moulds may be filled and emptied four or five times a day. After the cooling, the bottom plate of the cylinder is removed; the rollers drop out, are trimmed, and are ready for the shipping box.

LINE AND HALF-TONE PLATES

By George M. Gill

PRACTICALLY all book illustrations, as well as those in catalogs and periodicals of all kinds, are made by some method of photo-engraving. These quickly made and comparatively inexpensive process plates have not only taken the place of wood engraving but also increased the field of illustration to an enormous extent. They have made possible thousands of publications which could not have existed in the old days of the slow and costly wood engraving.

Photography is the basis of all the mechanical processes that come under the general head of photo-engraving. These processes are generally called mechanical, yet, as in photography, great skill is required to produce the best results. The higher grades of half-tone work require much careful finishing, which is all done by hand, and which, moreover, must be done by a skillful, intelligent, and artistic engraver. Practically all things may be reproduced successfully by photo-engraving, but the vast majority of subjects that go to the photo-engraver are either photographs or drawings.

Zinc etching is the simplest method of photo-engraving and should be thoroughly understood before one begins to inquire into the intricacies of the half-tone process. It is used to reproduce what is known as "black and white," or line drawings. Any drawing or print having black lines or dots on a white background, without any middle shades, may be engraved by this process. The old-fashioned "wet-plate" photography is used in making practically all process plates, either in line or in half-tone.

I will describe briefly all the operations gone through in making a line plate, taking for a subject a map drawn in black ink on white paper or a head drawn by James Montgomery Flagg—subjects wide apart in an artistic way, but of absolutely equal values so far as making the plate is concerned.

The drawing is first put on a copy board in front of a camera made especially for this work, in whose holder the wet plate has already been placed by the operator. The subject may be enlarged or reduced to any desired size, nearly all drawings being made much larger than they are desired to be reproduced in the plates. The exposure is much longer than in the ordinary dry plate work, generally lasting in the neighborhood of five minutes.

The result is a black and white negative. That is, the lines that were black in the drawing are absolutely clear and transparent in the negative, but the rest of the negative is black. From the photographer, the negative goes to the "negative-turning" room. Here the negative is coated with solutions of collodion and rubber cement, which makes the film exceedingly tough—so tough that it is easily stripped from the glass on which it was made, and is "turned" with the positive side up on another sheet of glass. If this were not done, the plate would be reversed in printing—that is, a line of type would read from right to left, or backward.

After the negative is "turned," it is ready for the etching room. Here the surface of a sheet of zinc about one-sixteenth of an inch thick, which has been polished until it is as smooth as plate glass and without a scratch or a flaw of any kind, is flowed with a sensitized solution, easily affected by light. The negative is placed in a printing frame over the sensitized zinc, and a print is made. That is, it is exposed to the sunlight or to a powerful electric light, and the light shines through the transparent parts of the negative and hardens the sensitized surface, while the black part of the negative protects the sensitized surface from the action of the light.

The plate is next "rolled up" with a lithograph roller which distributes a thin coating of etching ink over the entire surface. The plate is then washed off carefully by the operator, but the ink, which is greasy, adheres to all portions of the plate that have been acted upon by the light—that is, to the lines of the drawing. We now have a fully developed print on the highly polished surface of the zinc that is an exact reproduction of the original drawing.

It is now necessary to make this print acid proof,

and this is done by covering the plate with a coating of very fine resinous powder, called "dragon's blood," which adheres to the printed portions of the plate. The plate is subjected to enough heat to melt this powder, and is then ready for the acid bath.

A strong solution of nitric acid is used for etching zinc plates. This acid is placed in trays, which are rocked constantly, either by power or by hand, while the plate is being etched. The melted dragon's blood makes a perfect acid resistant, and the acid, therefore, does not affect the print (or picture, itself), but eats away the bare surfaces of the metal between the black lines and the dots. When this etching has proceeded far enough to make a plate that may be used in printing, the lines and dots of the picture stand up in bold relief, while the metal around these lines and dots has been eaten away to a considerable depth.

There are many details that cannot be described in a short article, but these are the principal operations gone through in etching the line plate. One very important detail in etching is to prevent "under-cutting." It is obvious that if the acid will eat downwards, it will also eat sidewise. The acid resistant is only on the surface. If means were not taken to prevent, the acid—as soon as it got below the surface—would begin to eat in under the print and the lines and dots of the picture would disappear; therefore, as soon as the plate has had its first "bite," it is taken from the acid, dried, and dragon's blood is brushed against the sides of the lines. This powder is then melted, and the plate given another etching. While the plate is being etched down, it is removed from the acid several times, and the sides of the dots and lines are again protected. After leaving the etching room the plate goes to the "router," an ingenious machine, with a cutting tool revolving at a speed of fourteen thousand revolutions a minute, which quickly removes the waste metal in the large open places between the lines and dots. The zinc plates are carefully looked over by a finisher, defects are removed, and the metal plates are then nailed on wooden blocks, so that they will be "type-high," that is, of exactly the same height as the metal type-forms used in printing. Hand presses are a necessity in all photo-engraving shops, and with these several "proofs" of each plate are printed in order that the customer may judge of the quality of the plate.

While the line, or zinc etching process is immensely useful in reproducing pen-and-ink drawings, maps, woodcut prints, etc., yet the half-tone process is the one that has practically revolutionized all known methods of illustration.

Although the zinc etching is limited in its capabilities to the reproduction of black and white subjects, practically everything in art or nature may be reproduced by the half-tone process. The half-tone "screen" makes it possible to take a photograph, or a wash drawing, and break the flat surface of the picture up into lines and dots with the white spaces between that are an absolute essential in relief plate printing. If a half-tone print taken from any magazine or periodical is examined closely, either with the naked eye or a magnifying glass, it will be seen that the entire picture is a network of lines and dots, and that there are two sets of lines running diagonally across the plate at right angles to each other. In the darker portions of the picture it will be seen that the lines are very heavy, with a small white dot in the center of each square, made by the intersecting lines. In the lighter portions of the picture, these lines will be found to be very fine, while in the lightest parts, or in the "high lights," as they are called, the lines disappear and in their places are a mass of fine dots, not much larger than a pin point.

To make a half-tone plate of a photograph or other subject, it is necessary to break the negative up into lines and dots. It is for this purpose that the half-tone "screen" is used. The screen consists of two thin pieces of plate glass, on the surface of which a series of very delicate parallel black lines have been ruled running diagonally across the glass. When these pieces of glass are placed together, face to face, the parallel lines ruled on them intersect each other at right angles, giving a very fine "mosquito-netting" effect. The method of making the negative is very similar to that described in making line negatives, excepting that in making a half-tone negative the screen is placed in the plate-holder directly in front of the negative. The subject is then photographed, and the result is a negative completely covered with a mass of fine transparent lines and dots.

Copper, instead of zinc, is generally used in making half-tone plates. In making a print on copper the light shines through the transparent lines and dots of the negative and hardens the sensitized surface of the plate. The black parts of the negative between the transparent lines and dots protect the sensitized surface. When the copper plate, after printing, is placed under a water tap, the parts of the sensitized surface that have not been acted upon by light wash away, leaving a print that becomes acid proof after being subjected to an intense heat.

The method of etching a copper plate is similar to that already described for etching zinc plates, excepting that sesquichloride of iron is used instead of nitric acid. In a half-tone the dots and lines are so close together that great depth is neither desirable nor possible, and no steps are taken to prevent undercutting.

The half-tone plate, after it has been carried as far as possible by mechanical processes, is capable of great improvement in the hands of skillful engravers. The plate as it comes from the etching bath may be termed a mechanical product. Though great skill is necessary in making the negative, the print, and the etching, the hand-finishing gives the plate many of its artistic qualities.

The unfinished plate is apt to be more or less "flat" in appearance; the high lights may not be light enough, while the dark portions of the plate are apt, in cases, to be too light. The most common methods of finishing are re-etching and burnishing. The finisher dips a

camel's-hair brush in acid and applies it to the high-light
portions of the plate or other places that are too dark,
and allows it to act on the metal until these parts of the
plate are lightened sufficiently. The parts of the plate
that are too light are made darker by rubbing down the
surface of the plate with a tool called the burnisher.
The skillful, artistic finisher has other methods at his
command of making the plate reproduce as accurately
and as artistically as possible the original drawing or
photograph. High-lights are sometimes cut out entirely,
or a very fine engraver's tool may be "run" between the
lines; while a "wood engraved" appearance is produced
by cutting, in certain portions of the plate, lines similar
to those used in wood engraving.

A point also worth remembering is that until the
plate reaches the finisher's hands, it has been more or less
of a mechanical product; and that the plate is made an
artistic creation by the skill, care, and brains of an unusually intelligent class of men.

The screens used in making half-tones represent a
considerable outlay in the large shops. A comparatively
small screen costs in the neighborhood of $150, while a
screen 18 x 20 inches, ruled 120 or 133 lines to the inch,
costs about $720. Screens are made with different num-
bers of lines to the inch and their use depends upon the
smoothness of the paper on which the cut is to be printed.
Those with 65 or 85 lines to the inch are for newspapers,
up to 133 for the average book work, and 175 and 200
for special illustrations on finely coated paper; inter-

mediate sizes are also used. A screen containing 200 lines to the inch is about the finest ever used for ordinary printing purposes; a few screens with 250, 300, and 400 lines to the inch have been made but are now almost never in demand. A well-equipped photo-engraving establishment must have many different screens.

In a well-managed shop, all of the cameras are in constant use in the daytime, and many are always in use all night. Some days the bulk of the work in the place will be a fine grade of magazine engraving calling for a fine screen. In order to keep all the cameras at work all the time, it is very important to have the number of fine screens almost equal to the number of cameras. The same is true of most of the other screens in general use. Fortunately for the engraver and the consumer, a screen, if it is carefully handled, will last a long time.

COLOR PLATE MAKING

By W. J. Wilkinson

THE reproduction, by means of the printing press, of photographs of colored objects is one of the most wonderful scientific achievements of the last century.

The records of the many experiments in many lands which contributed to its evolution, the important discoveries leading to its present state of perfection and the fortunes expended in its development, are still unwritten history that if fully covered, would fill many volumes.

When Roger Bacon, the leading scientist and philosopher of the thirteenth century, described the first camera, and Baptista Porta improved on it in 1500, they must have marveled at the beautiful colored images projected on the ground glass of the camera. But it was not until 1818 that Joseph Nicéphore Niepce of France began his experiments in an endeavor to fix those images. And later when Niepce's partner, Daguerre, showed in 1839, the camera image fixed upon a silvered mirror, the painters of France were seized with panic, and Paul Delaroche declared "Painting is dead from this day."

The Daguerreotype and the numerous photographic processes that followed it, recorded only lights and shadows. Fleeting color still evaded the scientist experimenter, and it was believed that it would never be possible to record it.   In 1869 another Frenchman, Louis Ducos du Hauron published a "Handbook of Heliochromy," in which he described the essentials necessary to success in reproducing the colored images of the camera. Du Hauron was ahead of his time and died in poverty. In 1873, Professor Vogel, of Germany, announced a manner of increasing the color-sensitiveness of photographic plates, and finally our own William Kurtz, an artist-photographer of New York, combined all the theories that had gone before and produced, in 1892, the first practical set of three-color blocks to record the colored images of the camera by the printing press.

Among the first to follow Kurtz in the photo-engraving of plates for reproducing in colors on the printing press was Gustav Zeese, whose practical experience at photo-engraving, electrotyping, and printing extended back to 1887.   Later, William J. Wilkinson took up the study of color plate making in Europe and became associated with Mr. Zeese in 1904 in the Zeese-Wilkinson Company which has specialized in making and printing color plates.

Color plates are made by what is known as the half-tone method which is described in another article in this book.   After the negative has been made through a half-tone screen, a photographic print is made on a properly sensitized sheet of polished metal which is etched with acid to bring the half-tone image into relief.

Reproductions in either three or four colors may be made from any colored original or object. As reduction is desirable, the original to be reproduced should be larger than the plate to be made. Water color drawings, pastels, or oil paintings are generally used as copy for magazine covers, book illustrations, and art prints, while carpets, textiles, and commercial objects are reproduced directly from the articles themselves.

The three-color process of photo-engraving and color printing is based upon the fact that by mixing in proper proportions the three primary colors,—yellow, red, and blue,—any hue gradations of color may be produced. In practice this is effected by engraving one plate to be used to print all the yellow of the picture, another to print all of the red, and a third to print all of the blue. Each plate is a separate half-tone made through a color filter, so that when each is printed in its correct color and in accurate register with the others, the result will closely resemble the original. The color filters used to get the yellow plate is green in color, that for the red is yellow, and that for the blue is red.

After some years of using the three-color method it was found that owing to the difficulty attending the reproduction of pictures containing neutral grays, and especially of retaining these shades on long press runs, it was advisable to add a black plate to the three primary colors. The majority of color reproductions are now made by this four-color process.

The method of analyzing a colored object so as to separate the three primary colors as well as the shades of which they are composed is briefly as follows: the copy to be reproduced by the three-color or the four-color process is placed before a specially constructed camera, and, after focusing to the desired dimensions, the operator proceeds to secure a set of color-record negatives, one for each of the colors to be printed later.

Each negative is made on a photographic plate sensitized according to the color which it is desired it shall record. With the aid of a carefully made filter of optically perfect colored glass, placed behind the lens, action by all the other colors is either greatly retarded or entirely prevented.

Each color negative records the values and gradations of the particular primary color for which it is made, and from the negative is engraved the plate which is to be printed in that color. These color negatives are usually called "color-separation" negatives. As in plain half-tone plates, much hand work can be, and usually is, done on the color plates to improve them.

There is no branch of photography which requires such highly skilled artisans as that of making color-separation negatives. Artistic judgment is required at every step in the operation, and it is absolutely necessary that those engaged in every department shall have normal color perception. Color blindness in varying degrees is more common than is generally known. While artists and engravers with defective color vision may be successful in an ordinary engraving establishment, they would be failures in the making of color process plates or the printing of them.

For the four-color process, there is a fourth photographic plate which records only the blacks and the neutral tones.

It is obvious that the rays which act on the photographic plate must be intense, therefore proper illumination of the original is important. Powerful electric arc-lamps are used, for daylight is generally entirely too weak and unreliable to act with sufficient energy upon the photographic plate. The period of exposure depends upon the nature of the original and the density of the colors it contains.

The exposures having been made, the negatives are developed and fixed in a dark room, examined, and compared with the original. The high-lights and shadow dots in the half-tone negatives must be of the proper size and density. In order to allow sufficient etching the high-light dots are made larger on the negative than required in the finished plate. If the dots are too dense, they may be reduced, or intensified if too weak. The negatives are then dried and are ready for printing in the manner described in the article on making half-tone plates.

Proofs of color plates are usually taken on universal presses on the paper to be used for the printing of the edition. The coating, color, and the finish of the various paper stocks are of great consequence in proving, and a set of plates which will show up splendidly on a fine piece of coated paper will appear entirely different on an inferior grade. Therefore if the edition is to be printed on the cheaper quality of paper, proofs submitted on the better stock will naturally tend to mislead the printer.

Considerable study has been given to the standardization and selection of proper printing inks for three- and four-color printing. It is very essential to prove with inks of the same hue as the inks to be used for printing the final edition.

Three-color plates are usually proved, the yellow first, the red second, and the blue last. For the four-color process the correct rotation is: yellow first, red second, blue third, and black last, although this rotation may sometimes be changed without jeopardizing the results. If the yellow is printed last, it must be with transparent ink. The red used for both processes is similar, but the blues vary considerably, four-color blue being more brilliant and of a lighter shade than that used for the three-color process. Each color should be allowed to dry perfectly before the next is applied.

It is an interesting fact that the different colors of a three- or four-color print meet in the eye of the observer, and not on the print itself.

The plates may be corrected after proving, if necessary, by re-etching and burnishing them to produce the desired effects, and new proofs should be pulled until the reproduction is satisfactory and can be matched by the printer. It is not feasible to finish a set of plates in one proving; and usually two, and often more, provings are made before the reproduction matches all the colors of the original. When finished, the plates are delivered to the customer, sent to the pressroom to be printed or to the foundry for electrotyping.

THE WAX PROCESS

By Robert D. Servoss

ALMOST all of the maps found in text and reference books, as well as the geometrical diagrams used in mathematical and scientific works, are made by what is known as the "wax process."

This process was invented and patented by an Englishman named Palmer about 1840, shortly after the discovery of the method of making electrotype plates for printing purposes. He announced that he would furnish artists with copper plates covered with a waxlike composition on which they could make their own drawings, in a manner similar to but much simpler than the method followed by the etcher on copper. After receiving the artist's work, the plates were to be returned to Palmer, who then made an ordinary electrotype of the engraving. A circular, issued about 1841, gives the necessary instructions for engraving, and the prices for the wax-coated plates and the subsequent electrotypes, and shows many beautiful illustrations made by artists of that time. It was then called the "glyphographic process."

The process was first introduced into this country by a firm of printers in Buffalo, New York, and was used by them for several years for illustrating the United States patent office reports until it was superseded upon the introduction of photo-lithography and the subsequent adoption by the government of a uniform standard for patent drawings.

This process may be described in a general way as follows: A copper plate having a highly polished surface is first blackened by the application of a weak solution of sulphuret of potassium, or other chemical which will oxidize the copper. Then a composition, made by melting together in proper proportions, beeswax, zinc-white, and paraffin, is "flowed" over the blackened surface, producing an opaque whitish engraving ground. The thickness of the wax is varied according to the subject to be engraved, but in general should not exceed that of heavy writing paper. After it has been allowed to cool with the plate lying perfectly horizontal, the wax is smoothed down to an even thickness by a steel scraper, and the plate is then ready to receive the engraving.

Taking for an example the engraving of a map, the original copy is either photographed on the wax surface, or is transferred to it by covering the back of the copy with red chalk and tracing over every line with a steel point. The photograph, or the tracing, on the wax must not be a reversed one, as might be supposed, but should "read right." The outlines of the map are then gone over, with an engraving tool which cuts out a small channel in the wax, down to, but not into, the surface of the copper plate. The bottoms of these channels will eventually form the surface of the relief lines in the resultant electrotype plate, but now appear as dark lines against the whitish ground-work of the wax.

The engraving tools are made in different sizes, and therefore channels of varying widths at the bottoms may be cut in order to produce lines of different sizes. In cutting lines to indicate rivers,—which must be thin at the source and increase in thickness as they approach the mouth,—tools are used in graduated sizes. The first one cuts its own line of equal width for a very short distance, then another and slightly wider tool is used, the next still wider, and so on until the river line is completed. In reality a series of steps, the work is so done that the line appears to the eye to increase in width evenly and gradually from a very fine beginning to a heavy ending. The wavy lines indicating hills and mountains are made in substantially the same way. Special steel punches are pressed through the wax to the copper to show town and capital marks, and after all the lines and marks are completed, the plate is ready to receive the lettering. The name of each individual town, city, state, or river is set up in printer's type and stamped one name at a time into the wax. The type is placed in a small tool resembling a vise, which holds it in perfect alignment and on a perfect level. Tools of various shapes are used for stamping the names in straight and curved lines. It is necessary to wet the type to prevent its adhering to the wax.

The plate is then carefully compared with the

original copy and after any necessary corrections have been made it is gone over by an expert operator, who cuts out any of the channels which may have been obliterated by the burr of the wax, resulting from pressing in the names.

We now have a plate in which the lines have been cut in small channels and the names stamped with type. This is a matrix, or mould, from which an electrotype of the lines now sunken in the wax may be made in high relief for printing, but the blank portions of the wax are so thin that it is first necessary to fill in all these places on the plates with wax in order to produce a sufficiently deep electrotype plate. This is done by "building up" the plate. A small hook-shaped tool, heated over a gas jet, is used to melt small pieces of wax which are run carefully around all the names and in the spaces between lines, thus filling up all these spaces with a round, smooth body of wax. From this mould an ordinary electrotype is made by the method described elsewhere in this book.

All these operations require much skill and patience at every step, but the plates produced by the wax process are always much deeper and stronger than those made by any other process.

MAKING INTAGLIO PLATES

By Elmer Latham

THE method by which a photogravure plate is produced, is probably the least understood of all of the many photo-processes of reproduction. This is chiefly on account of the difficulty of the process, which is not an easy matter to explain in detail, and also on account of the secrecy with which many plate makers guard their processes.

The reproduction of a mezzotint or line-engraved print, when made by a good photogravure process, produces in most cases a print which cannot be detected from the original. The originator of the process was probably Fox Talbot, an Englishman. The writer has seen one of his prints, made between 1855 and 1860, which was a very creditable piece of work. Dujardin of Paris took up Talbot's process, and after many modifications, succeeded in developing a successful process which is much used today. All photogravure plate makers have more or less copied the process of Fox Talbot.

There are three different methods of making these plates known to the writer. The reader probably knows that a photogravure plate is not a relief plate, but an intaglio, and is printed on an etching-press in the same manner as an etching and requires special skill in printing on the part of the printer to produce the best results. I will give a brief explanation of three different processes for making photogravures.

The first is known as the transfer process. In this process a reversed photographic negative is made from the copy, from which a positive or "transparency" is made, either by contact or in the camera. A piece of carbon paper is coated lightly with gelatine, sensitized with bichromate of potassium and allowed to dry. The paper is then placed in contact with the positive and printed in daylight until the image is imprinted on the gelatine coating of the paper, such portions of which as have received the most exposure from the action of light becoming quite insoluble. A copper plate, cleaned so that it is free from grease, is introduced into a large box into which has been blown a very finely powdered resin, which is allowed to settle somewhat before putting in the plate. The plate is allowed to remain in the box until a fine deposit of resin has settled all over it. It is then carefully removed and heated over a gas burner until the resin adheres firmly to the plate. The resin is melted only to such a point that it forms a fine grain all over the plate, leaving interstices of bare copper between. The paper, on the gelatine surface of which the picture has been printed, is now placed in a tray of warm water, and the parts of the image which have had the least exposure are thereby dissolved and washed away, the image being thus fully developed on the paper. This is placed in contact with the grained plate, which has been placed in the tray of water, and firmly squeezed in contact with the plate. The paper is stripped off, leaving the gelatine film on the copper. The copper plate is now removed from the tray and dried, and is then ready for etching, which is accomplished by placing the plate successively in several baths of acid of different strengths until the desired results are obtained. This process gives a shallow plate, with little wearing quality, and, as a rule, requires a great deal of work by the engraver to bring the plate up to anything like the copy. The light tints come out very soft and smooth, but the black tones etch "flat" and lose all detail. The blacks must be put in by hand, and the poor wearing qualities of these plates make them undesirable in cases where a large edition has to be printed.

A second process is the "deposited" plate originally used by "Goupil" of Paris, in which copper is deposited by electricity upon a swelled gelatine film which has had a grain formed upon its surface chemically or otherwise. The deposition has to be continued until the plate has acquired the necessary thickness, which takes about three weeks; and this is a long time to wait in these days, when a publisher usually expects his order executed in a few days. These plates are practically hand made. The method produces a plate that could not possibly be used without a great deal of retouching by an expert engraver. Goupil turned out a beautiful plate, due principally to a large force of engravers, one man working on a particular part of the plate, then passing it on to another who does some other portion, and so on, until the plate is finished. In this way each engraver becomes exceedingly skillful in one thing. Line engraving is reproduced by this process exceedingly well, but such plates, like the transfer process, are shallow and soon give out in the printing.

The last process that I have to mention is the process in which the plates are made in two or more etchings, according to the requirements of the subject which is to be reproduced. This method produces a plate of great depth both in the light and black tints, and on account of the small amount of handwork required after the plate is etched, the copy is followed very closely. With a good positive and favorable conditions, quite frequently a plate is made upon which the retoucher needs to do no work at all, and a more faithful reproduction is made than by any of the other methods mentioned. After a good positive is procured, the copper plate is cleaned, and a sensitized solution of gelatine is flowed over the plate, dried down, and then printed under the positive, with a short exposure. The plate is grained as in the transfer process, and is then etched.

This first etching, on account of the short exposure, goes over the plate in about three minutes, and is simply intended to get the light tints. The plate is again cleaned off and coated, this time in a different manner, and given a much longer exposure under the positive. The next etching takes about three hours, which gives the blacks great depth.   Comparing this with the transfer plate which has an etching of from fifteen to twenty minutes, the reason for the difference in the wearing qualities of the plate is quite evident.   This process is the best one that has ever been worked, inasmuch as it gives a far more faithful reproduction than any of the others with a minimum of work by the retoucher.

Some plate makers claim to make all their plates without any retouching, which cannot be done, though occasionally a plate can be made as good as the copy without handwork.   But to say that any chemical process gives such results continually, or that a plate cannot be improved by a skillful retoucher is, to say the least, misleading.   All of the different processes are very sensitive to atmospheric influences, and no small amount of chemical as well as mechanical skill is required to keep things running smoothly; and at certain times the best of operators are at a loss to remedy some slight fault that may upset things temporarily.   Photogravure making is based upon a foundation of small details, that must be looked after with the utmost care, and the neglect of any one of which means failure at the end.   So it may be surmised that at times the operator has trouble of his own.

Every maker of plates, no matter which process he uses, has his individual ways of doing things, so that except in a general way no two processes are operated alike.   This gives an individuality to each man's work, and an expert can easily tell one from another.

The fine old methods of etching, mezzotint, and steel engraving are still occasionally used in the illustration of fine books, and brief descriptions of how they are made belongs to the story of intaglio plates.

An etching is usually made on a copper plate. The plate being covered with a thin coating of wax, the artist works on it with an etching point, sketching his subject on the plate in fine lines as he would in making a pen-and-ink drawing, but cutting his lines through to the copper. The plate is then "walled in" with a high rim of wax, forming a sort of tray of the plate. Into this tray is poured a diluted solution of nitric acid, which etches, or "bites," into the uncovered lines on the plate. Some artists give a plate a short "bite," as the etching is called, for the light lines, then cover these portions of the plate with wax and give the plate successive "bites," stopping out each part as it gains its required depth. Others remove the coating and "prove" the plate by taking a print from it after each "bite,"—each of these prints being known as a "state of the plate" and showing what is still required to be done. In the work of an etcher like Whistler the impressions of the "first state," "second state," etc., are of considerable interest, as they show the progress of the man's work, but, except as an object of interest or as a curiosity, these prints can have no real value as they are unfinished work, simply showing the various stages in the making of a work of art.

A mezzotint is also usually made on a copper plate. A texture, or groundwork, is worked on the copper plate with a tool resembling a cabinet maker's toothed plane iron, except that it is rounded at the end. The teeth are very fine, ranging from forty to one hundred and twenty to the inch in different tools. This tool is called a "Bercier," or "rocker." The rounded edge allows the tool to be rocked across the plate, the rocking motion causing the teeth to form indentations in the copper. The rocking has to be continued until the surface of the plate is completely covered, and it then presents an appearance like velvet. Rocking in from forty to sixty directions is necessary to cover the plate properly. The durability of a mezzotint plate depends entirely upon the pressure put upon the rocker, and the depth to which it penetrates the copper. After the ground is thus laid, the outline is sketched in on the rocked surface, which takes the pencil easily, and then with steel scrapers and burnishers the light and middle tints are worked down, leaving undisturbed the portions of the surface where the strongest blacks are to be. From time to time, a print is taken from the plate, to note the progress of the work, which advances slowly to the finish. On account of the length of time necessary for the laying of the ground and the scraping of the plate, many artists hesitate to attempt mezzotint plates. There are very few men in this country today who do mezzotint engraving, which, considering the results to be obtained, seems somewhat surprising.

For flesh tones, drapery, and landscapes it has no equal. The velvety richness of the blacks, the beautiful gradations of the middle tones, and the extreme delicacy of the light tints give the artist a power of expression not obtainable by any other method of engraving. Besides this, as the engraving is done on the bare copper, the artist can see at all times the progress of his work without having to take off the wax ground as he must in making an etching. This is a great advantage, for as the effect of each stroke can be plainly seen on the plate, the element of uncertainty which always attends the production of an etching is entirely eliminated, and it is then simply a question of skill with the scraper. The difficulty of obtaining rockers is one great drawback. The teeth have to be very accurately cut, and a perfect tool has a value to an engraver that cannot well be estimated. The lack of demand has prevented their manufacture in this country, but they could be made here by any fine tool maker.

Steel engravings are now little used in this country. A wax ground is laid on the plate as in etching. A tracing is made from the photograph, from which the picture is to be made, and is then transferred to the wax ground. The engraver then follows the lines of the tracing with an etching point, the hair, head, and outline of the features being gone over carefully. Then the plate is etched with weak nitric acid. If the face is to be "stippled," it is covered with fine dots made by a graver directly on the surface of the metal after the plate has been etched and the wax cleaned off. If the face is to be a mezzotint, that part of the work is all rocked over, and then scraped down within the etched outline, when the flesh is modeled as in a regular mezzotint. The drapery, background, etc., is usually done by a ruling machine with fine or coarse, waved or straight lines, as the texture may require. These lines are ruled through a coating of wax, and then, by etching and stopping out, the required results are obtained.

This method of engraving is also giving place to process work, and in a few years more the steel engraved portrait will probably be a thing of the past.

PRINTING INTAGLIO PLATES

By George W. H. Ritchie

THE method of printing etchings, mezzotint, and other intaglio plates is the same today as it was in the time of Rembrandt and Dürer. The modern inventor has found no way to economize time, labor, or expense in the work—excepting that in the case of postage stamps, bond certificates, and similar plates, which are printed in vast quantities, the work has been adapted to the steam press.

In the olden time the engraver, or etcher, was to a considerable extent his own printer. He worked at engraving his plate until he needed a proof to show him how the work was progressing. Then he printed, or "pulled," a proof and resumed his work, taking proofs from time to time until he had completed the plate to his satisfaction. Then, if only a small edition was required, he printed it. Proofs taken during the making of a plate are known by plate engravers and printers as the "states" of a plate, and it is due to the whim of the etcher, the softness of the copper, and the wearing of the plate in printing that we have prints representing many "states" of a single plate which might otherwise have had but one state, thus depriving one modern print collector of the privilege of discovering in his proof three hairs more or less in a donkey's tail than his rival finds in another proof, which makes the former's more valuable by several hundred pounds.

One form of press is used for all manner of intaglio plate printing. It consists of a framework supporting two heavy iron rollers, between which moves a flat iron traveling plank, or bed, and on this bed the plate to be printed is laid. The pressure of the rollers is regulated by screws at each end of the top roller, which is covered with two or three pieces of thick felt. This top roller is revolved by handles and the bed moves along with it under the pressure of the roller. At one side of the press stands a rectangular box, or "stove," made of iron, or having an iron top. The top is heated and on it the printer puts his plate while inking and wiping it. The heat thins the ink as it is applied, allowing it to be worked freely and to be "lifted" easily by the paper.

The ink is made of fine bone dust, vegetable or other form of carbon, which has been carefully cleansed from foreign matter and ground to the necessary fineness in combination with burned linseed oil. Its strength and consistency should be varied according to the plate which is in hand, and the color also may be varied to suit the character of the plate by the addition of pigments.

The paper used in plate printing may be one of several kinds, but the usual variety is a fine white paper free from spots and imperfections which might mar the appearance of the finished print.   This paper is made either by hand or machinery of selected bleached cotton rags, and has a soft, spongy surface which yields readily under the pressure of the plate.   Before it can be used the paper is moistened and allowed to stand for from one to twelve hours, or even longer, until it becomes evenly and thoroughly dampened,—but not wet,—so that it will more readily force itself into the lines of the plate and take therefrom and hold the ink.

Before printing a photogravure, mezzotint, or other engraved plate the printer must first carefully examine it to see that it has no scratches, and that no dried ink remains in the lines from the last printing, and, in fact, that there are none of the many possible impedimenta which might prevent the production of a perfect print. The plate being in proper condition, it is then thoroughly cleansed with turpentine or benzine, all traces of which must be carefully wiped from the surface before the ink is applied.   The plate is then laid on the heated iron box or "stove" until it has become thoroughly warmed.   The surface of the plate is covered with ink, put on by means of an ink-roller, or perhaps the old-fashioned dauber, and the ink is thoroughly worked into the lines or depressions in the plate.   After this the ink on the flat surface of the plate is entirely removed by wiping with rags.   The printer's hand, which has become more or less covered with ink from the rags, is then passed over a piece of chalk, or gilder's white, and lightly rubbed over the surface of the plate, to remove the last vestige of the ink, leaving a highly polished flat surface with the incised lines or depressions filled with ink to the level of the surface.

The plate is then ready for printing and is placed on the bed of the press, a sheet of dampened paper laid upon it, and both are then run between the rollers of the press. As the top roller is encased in soft blankets, the soft, dampened paper is forced into the ink-filled lines of the plate, and when the paper is removed the ink clings to it and shows an exact impression of the engraving. This entire process must be repeated for each print made from an intaglio plate.

While the printing of a steel engraving or photogravure is a more or less mechanical operation, the printing of an etching—and "dry points" may be included— is oftentimes as much of an art as the actual etching of the plate. The two styles of printing may be compared to two kinds of fishing,—that of fishing for flounders with a drop line, from a flat-bottomed boat at low tide when one must just sit tight until one has a bite, and then haul in the fish, bait up, drop the line and wait again, as against that of angling for trout on an early spring day, dropping the fly in a likely spot without success at the first cast, persevering until rewarded by a rise and then by the sport of playing the fish, giving him line and reeling him in as he circles about, and finally is landed. A good one, perchance, but the sport was in landing him. So it is with printing an etching. There is the opportunity to play with, and work hard over, a plate. Perhaps the etcher has not, for reasons only known to himself, put in the plate all that can be shown in the print by ordinary printing. The printer actually has to interpret in his printing the etcher's meaning, for the which, as a rule, he gets "more kicks than ha'pence," and in the end wishes he had stuck to plain plate printing as far as the profit is concerned.

In the process of printing an etching, the printer first covers the plate with ink and then wipes it with the rags, and, if necessary, with the hand. It depends entirely upon the etched work of the plate as to how it must be wiped, and it rests with the printer to prepare a proof which is satisfactory to the etcher. The plate is wiped "closely" where the high lights are required or a tint (a thin coating of ink) left over certain portions where it needs to be darker. After this the plate is "retroussed," which is accomplished by passing a very soft piece of fine muslin, or a "badger blender,"—a soft brush used by artists,—delicately over the work in the plate and drawing the ink up and over the edges of the lines. This softens and broadens the lines and gives a very rich effect, and, if continued sufficiently, fills the spaces between the lines and produces an almost black effect. All this work is varied according to the wishes of the etcher. A plate that left the etcher's hand a mere skeleton may be made to produce a print which is a thing of life. The possibilities of an etching in the hands of a skillful printer are almost limitless; the effects can vary with every impression, each showing a new picture. His processes are as interesting as those of the etcher himself, and it is within his capabilities to transform an etching from a broad daylight effect into a moonlight scene, including the moon, by judiciously, or injudiciously, inking and wiping the plate.

A "dry point" plate is produced by drawing on a copper plate with a steel or diamond point, and without biting by acid. The lines are cut into the copper and a burr thrown up which holds the ink in printing, and produces a soft, velvety line. The method of printing such a plate is similar to that of an etching, but the possibilities are not as great in the printing, as they rest to a greater extent upon the work of the artist. A great depth of color, producing wonderfully rich effects, can be obtained and the finer lines can be made much more delicate than by any other method.

The printing of intaglio plates in color flourished for a short period in the latter portion of the eighteenth century, and the best prints of that time now in existence are of rare beauty and bring enormous prices. The process is a costly one, and this prevents its use in book illustration excepting for volumes which command a very high price. This kind of printing requires the plate to be actually painted by hand with inks of such colors as the picture may require, and the painting has to be repeated for every impression that is taken. The colors are put on with a "dole,"—a small piece of muslin turned to a point,—and great care must be taken that they do not overlap, or run into, each other. As each color is placed, the plate is wiped clean with rags as already described, and when all the colors have been properly placed, the plate is pulled through the press in the same manner as in ordinary printing.

The successful printer of color plates must be a rare artist or else work under the direction of an artist.

It is difficult to describe the work of what is termed artistic printing. Every plate is a subject to be treated by itself, and no hard and fast rule can be applied. It is really a matter of artistic feeling, and to revert to the simile of the angler, one cannot explain how a trout should be played, but can only say that it depends on the fish, the water, and the circumstances. A fisherman can *show* you, if you are on the spot, and so can the printer.

LITHOGRAPHY

By Charles Wilhelms

IT may not be generally known, and yet of sufficient interest to the reader to state, that the art of lithography, or surface printing, was invented accidentally. The inventor, Aloys Senefelder, had been engaged for years endeavoring to find some process for etching copper plates as a substitute for typographic printing plates; and the piece of stone (of a kind now known as Solenhofen lithographic stone) which eventually led him to the discovery of lithography had been used by him as a slab upon which he had been accustomed to grind his printing ink. The materials which he used for his acid-resisting mixture while etching his copper plates were beeswax, soap, and lampblack, and in selecting these materials he accidentally invented the basis for all crayons or lithographic "tusche" or inks, now used so extensively for drawing on stone. It seems that Senefelder finally became thoroughly disheartened about his etched copper plates, mainly owing to the great expense and labor connected with their production, and was about to discontinue his efforts when the idea occurred to him to experiment with the stone which he had used as an ink slab for so many months, treating it in the same manner as the copper plates.

He knew that the calcareous stone was easily affected by acid and that he could protect the surface against it by a layer of wax. After polishing the surface of the stone and coating it with a slight layer of wax, he made his drawing with a pointed tool, laying bare the surface of the stone where he desired the engraving. Then applying the acid and removing the remaining wax, he filled the etched lines with printing ink, cleaned the surface of the stone with water, and was enabled to obtain an impression on paper from it. This manner of treating a stone has been employed by vignette engravers for many years, but of late has become obsolete. The result gave encouragement to Senefelder and induced him to renew his experiments, when he was accidentally led a step farther in the direction of surface or chemical printing.

Senefelder had just ground and polished a stone, when his mother entered the room and asked him to take a memorandum of some clothes which she was about to send away to be laundered. Having neither paper nor ink at hand, he hastily wrote the items with a pen, dipped in his acid-resisting mixture, upon the stone which had just been polished. When he afterwards started to wipe the writing from the stone, it occurred to him that it might be possible to reverse his process by etching the surface of the stone, leaving the writing or drawing in relief, which could be printed from in the same manner as from type. He was fairly successful in this, and after many disappointments and much hardship, he eventually succeeded in interesting a capitalist, with whose assistance he was enabled to establish his new relief stone process on a commercial basis.

The process, however, was at best only an imperfect one, and it seems strange that the final discovery of surface or lithographic printing should have been so long delayed, when Senefelder was in reality so near it, when he first poured the acid over the stone containing his laundry memorandum. If he had instantly washed off the acid and cleaned the surface of the stone with water, he might have proceeded to print thousands of impressions by simply keeping the surface of the stone moist while passing the ink roller or dabber over it, then drying and taking an impression, and repeating this operation indefinitely.

It is not surprising, therefore, that a man of such persistence and capability as Senefelder should eventually discover the best method for drawing and printing from stone; for it is a fact that, since he perfected his invention, more than a hundred years ago, it has been hardly possible to improve on his methods, so completely did he cover the entire field of manipulation in this direction. Continuing his experiments, Senefelder finally found that the calcareous stone absorbed and held grease, and that it just as readily absorbed water where the surface was exposed and clean; that any design drawn or transferred with a greasy crayon or ink upon a cleanly polished stone would be firmly held after being slightly etched; and that after such a stone had been moistened, it could be inked with rollers, the ink adhering only to the greasy matter constituting the design (although it did not stand out in the relief) and that the ink rollers would not smut the stone, the ink being repelled by the water or moisture covering its surface. Upon this principle of chemical affinity, the adherence of greasy substances to each other and the antipathy of grease and water, the art of lithographic printing is based.

The methods or processes now employed in reproducing oil-paintings, colored photographs, or water-colors by lithography are numerous, and require great skill and experience, not only on the part of the lithographic artist, but also on the part of the printer. Photography has of late years been used to a great extent in creating the basis of the color plates, to be afterwards perfected by the manipulation of the experienced chromo-lithographer.

To insure a satisfactory result the first essential is, of course, a good original, which may be made in water-color, oil, or pastel. The number of printings to be employed should be predetermined and a color scale adopted. The lithographer must carefully analyze the original painting, making his calculations as to the best way of obtaining the desired color effects by a judicious selection and use of his colors, and the superimposing of one printing over the other, so as to obtain true color values. It must be remembered that, while the average painter has an unlimited variety of pigments at his disposal, the lithographer is in this respect very much at a disadvantage, usually not having more than from six to fourteen colors with which to produce a facsimile of the original.

The first step is the making of the so-called key-plate. A piece of gelatine is laid on the original, which is, let us say by way of illustration, a water-color to be reproduced in ten printings, and a careful tracing of the original is made by scratching, with an engraving needle, the outline of each wash or touch of color composing the picture. This being completed, the lithographic ink (tusche) or transfer ink is carefully rubbed into the tracing, which is laid face down on a polished lithographic stone, slightly moistened, and passed through a hand press thereby transferring the ink from the engraved lines to the polished surface of the stone. The design on the stone is then "rolled in" with black printing ink and etched, thus enabling the lithographer to take the necessary ten impressions of the key-plate. These, in their turn, are again transferred to as many lithographic stones. This is accomplished by dusting the impressions with a red powder, which adheres only to the design printed on the sheet. The powdered outline design is then transferred to the surface of the stone by passsing both through a hand press. The key has been previously provided with register marks (a short horizontal line intersected by a vertical one) at top, bottom, and both sides. These are of the utmost importance to the prover, and finally to the transferrer, who prepares the work for the press, as without them it would be impossible to register one color over the other in its proper place. At any stage of the process, the register marks of all ten colors, when printed successively on a single sheet of paper, should coincide precisely and appear as a single mark in the form of a small cross.

The lithographer now has before him the ten stones, each stamped with the identical network of lines in red chalk representing his key. He proceeds to draw each color plate successively, at all times adhering closely to the red chalk outlines, filling in with tusche where full strength of the color is required and using lithographic crayon or the stipple process to reproduce the various gradations of this color in order to secure the full color value of each printing. The register marks are ruled in on each stone corresponding to those on the key, so that the prover or printer has these marks in the same identical position on each and every color as a guide for register.

As each stone is finished it is etched; that is, treated with a weak solution of nitric acid and gum-water, in order to remove all accidental traces of scum from its surface and to prepare it for printing. Then proofs are made, which serve as a guide to the lithographer during the progress of his work, and finally as a guide to the transferrer and to the printer. The proving is done on a hand press, and it is here that we have our first glimpse of chemical printing, which, notwithstanding its simplicity, seems so mysterious to one uninitiated in its secrets.

The writer recollects his own first experience. A stone had just been placed fresh from the etching trough in the bed of the press, when, to his amazement, the prover deliberately proceeded to eliminate every trace of the drawing with a sponge saturated with turpentine. After drying the stone by means of a fan, he passed over the surface a sponge soaked in water, then applied black ink with a roller, when behold, the drawing was restored in its entirety. The explanation is very simple: the greasy matter is absorbed and held by the stone and in its turn repels water and attracts grease.

An impression is made with black printing ink on paper by passing it through the hand press. The black impression approved by the lithographer, the stone is again cleaned with turpentine and proved in the color required, and so with each color plate, until the proof is complete. When photography is employed, the half-tone negative takes the place of the key. Prints are made from a reversed negative on the sensitized surface of the stone, or on as many stones as the color plates require, and then manipulated by the lithographer, who adds or modifies strength with his "tusche" or crayon, and scrapes or washes out lights where necessary. The various modes of procedure are too diverse to enter into here, but it may be well to mention that the principal ones are the albumen, the asphaltum, and finally the three- or four-color processes, the latter differing but little as far as the artistic part of the work is concerned from that employed for making relief printing plates for the typographic press, which is described elsewhere in this book.

The original drawing plates, or stones, are not used to print from direct unless the edition be very small. Just as the typographic printer uses electrotypes in place of the original type or cuts, the lithographer makes transfers from the original stones to print his edition and carefully preserves the original stones for future editions. The transfers are prepared in a very simple manner. The original stones are rolled over with a specially prepared transfer ink, and impressions are taken from them on a paper, known under the name of transfer paper, coated with a sizing of starch, flour, and glycerine. By printing from the original, only one copy can be produced at each impression, whereas by using transfers a number of copies of the original can be printed at one impression. For example, if the picture measures 8 x 10 inches of paper, a transfer can be made containing fifteen copies on one sheet measuring 30 x 40 inches. In this case fifteen impressions are made from the key-plate as well as from each of the color plates, on the paper, and with the ink.

The first transfer to be made is that of the key-plate. The fifteen impressions are laid in their proper positions on a sheet of paper of the required size, and are held in position on the same by indentations made with a dull-pointed steel tool. The sheet is laid face down upon a cleanly polished stone, which is then repeatedly pulled through a hand press until all the ink has been transferred from the paper to the surface of the stone. The transfer paper still adhering to the stone is then moistened and washed off the stone, leaving the design completely transferred to the stone. A slight solution of gum arabic and water is then applied, the stone is washed clean, and after being repeatedly rolled in with printing ink and etched, is ready for printing.

An impression is then made in the usual manner from this key-transfer, which impression is coated with a solution of shellac. This is done for the purpose of rendering it impervious to the effect of the atmosphere, thus insuring against its stretching or shrinking. Upon this varnished key-sheet all subsequent transfer impressions of the ten colors are "stuck up," to use the technical term, and transferred to stone in the same manner as is employed in the making of the key-transfer. The register marks serve as a guide in "sticking up" the separate transfer impressions and insure an accurate register of the colors laid over each other during the process of printing. New register marks are placed upon the key-transfer at top, bottom, and sides similar to those on the original (which are removed from the transfer), and these new marks now appear on all color transfers to serve as a guide to the pressman in printing his edition. He likewise uses the hand-press proofs of the picture as a guide in selecting or mixing his inks.

The lithographic power printing press is constructed on the same general principle as the ordinary typographic press, excepting that it is provided with an apparatus for moistening the stone previous to the application of the ink rollers. The stone containing the design is placed in the bed of the press, and the moisture, as well as the ink, is applied by means of rollers similar to those used in the typographic printing press. All the ten colors are now successively printed on a power press, and if it is a perfect job, the pictures can be cut to size and delivered to the publisher.

The introduction of flexible plates made of zinc or aluminum, in place of cumbersome lithographic stones, has made possible the use of rapid rotary presses which can print at one operation two, three, and even four colors.

A further development came with the offset process which differs from lithographic printing in that, instead of the paper's receiving the impression directly from the printing plate, the cylinder carrying the plate comes in contact with a special cylinder covered with a rubber blanket, which receives the impression and in turn transmits it to the paper.

One of the advantages of this newer method lies in the fact that the paper, itself, does not come in contact with the moistened printing plate, obviating many difficulties that had previously been caused by the stretching of the paper, owing to the absorption of moisture.

The characteristic beauty of offset work, however, is, in itself, its justification, and coupled with the advantages of more economical production because of the rotary press, the process marks an epoch in the development of the lithographic art. It enables lithography to compete with the typographic four-color process, which for a time threatened to supplant lithography entirely as a medium for the reproductions of certain classes of work.

Experience teaches us, therefore, that the surface, or lithographic, and the relief, or typographic, processes will never seriously interfere with each other, but on the contrary, by actively competing in all matters relating to the reproductive art, will continue to improve their respective methods and thus aid in satisfying the continually increasing demand for colored illustrations, both as to the quantity production and, especially, as to the quality.

THE GELATINE PROCESS

By Emil Jacobi

With revisions by Chester P. Jones

OF the many photo-mechanical processes which have
come into existence in recent years, the photo-
gelatine, next to the half-tone process, has shown the
greatest adaptability for practical use in art and com-
merce.

Whatever the name may be,—collotype, photo-
gelatine, or gelatine gravure,—the principle is the same;
an impression is made in printer's ink from a photo-
chemically produced design on a gelatine surface, either
on the hand press or on a power cylinder press similar
to that used in lithographic printing.

There is hardly any process which is more capable
of producing fine works of art. It is the only true
method for reproducing, in the full sense of the word, an
etching, engraving, a drawing in pen and ink, an
aquarelle, a painting, or objects from nature. The depth
and richness of tone of an engraving, the delicate tints of
an aquarelle or india-ink sketch, and the sharpness of the
lines of an etching or pen sketch can be reproduced with

such fidelity that it is often impossible to distinguish the copy from the original, and this is achieved the more easily as the printing can be done in any color and on any material, be it paper, parchment, leather, or textile goods.

Another great advantage of a gelatine print is its inalterability and durability, no chemicals being employed in transferring the picture to the paper. The picture itself being formed by solid pigments, such as are used in printer's ink or painter's colors, there is no possibility of its fading or changing color, which cannot be said even of platino prints, at present considered the most lasting of all photo-chemical processes.

Like all inventions, the photo-gelatine process, in its early stages, had to undergo severe trials, and for some years almost disappeared from public view, after many failures precipitated through unscrupulous promoters and inefficient persons who claimed impossibilities for the new process. It took years of patience and perseverance to regain the lost ground and overcome the opposition of those who had suffered by the failure of this process to produce the promised results; but at present it is, in Europe, one of the methods in most general use for illustrating, and in this country it is making steady progress and rapidly finding favor.

The process, simple as it may seem to the casual observer, requires, more than any other photo-mechanical process, skilled hands in its different manipulations to keep it up to the standard of perfection. The following

short description will give the uninitiated sufficient en-
lightenment to think and speak intelligently about it.

The foundation or starting point, as of all the other
photo-mechanical processes, is a photographic negative;
that is, a picture on glass or some other transparent substance, in which the light parts of the picture appear
dark, and the dark parts light in transparency, graduated
according to the different shades of tone in the original.
The next and most prominent feature is the printing
plate. A perfectly even glass, copper, or zinc plate is
covered on the surface with a solution of fine gelatine
and bichromate of potassium, and dried. This printing
plate is then placed under a negative and exposed to the
light. The action of the light on the bichromated gelatine forms the basis of this process. In proportion to the
graduated density of the negative, the light acts more or
less on the bichromated gelatine, rendering the latter, in
proportion, insoluble and hardening it. After sufficient
exposure the plate is washed out in water to eliminate
the bichromate not acted upon by the light, and is then
actually ready for the press.

If the printing is to be done on a hand press, a lithographic leather roller is charged with printer's ink, and
the plate, which has been fastened on a suitable bed-
plate in the press, is rolled up while it is still moist.
Those parts of the plate which were acted upon by the
light and hardened, repel the water and take up the ink,
and thus all the graduating tones, up to the high lights or
white parts, which have not been affected by the light,

will take the ink proportionately. The white parts of the picture, where the light did not act upon the gelatine during the exposure under the negative, retain the natural property of gelatine to absorb water, and consequently repel the ink altogether.

From the foregoing it will be easy to understand that a certain degree of moisture in the plate is necessary to get a correct impression. After the leather roller, a composition roller, such as is used in typographical processes, is employed to make the ink smooth and give the fine details not obtainable from the rough surface of a leather roller. A sheet of paper is then placed upon the plate and by pressure the ink is transferred from the plate to the paper.

The printing, in former years, could only be done on hand presses; but with the introduction of improved power presses especially adapted to it the process itself has been so perfected that the finest work can be executed on them, at the same time insuring greater evenness and increased quantity of production, and also admitting the use of larger plates than would be possible on a hand press.

The prevailing impression, whenever machinery is employed to supersede handwork, is that the production is increased to such an extent as to reduce the cost to a minimum, but in the gelatine printing process, even with the aid of power presses, the rapidity of printing is far behind the possibilities of the lithographic or typographical printing press. The process, however, is especially applicable to works of art, and the better grade of illustrations in literary and commercial publications, and is being used to a large extent in place of photogravures on copper and genuine photographs.

The lesser rapidity of production and the greater cost is balanced by the quality, where this item comes into consideration; and where only small editions are required, even the cost compares favorably with other methods, as the initial cost of preparing the printing plate is small compared with the cost of photogravure or the better class of half-tone plate. It is only in cases of large editions of many thousands that the advantage of rapid printing reduces the cost of the initial expense. But fine art publications and illustrations will never be used in very large quantities, and, therefore, there is a large field for the photo-gelatine process in this country where it is being developed and is helping the user of small quantities of reproductions by giving him high grade prints at a saving in cost as compared with other reproduction processes. In France, Germany, and Austria there are dozens of establishments which employ ten or more power presses for photo-gelatine work, while here only within the last few years has the process been sufficiently appreciated to warrant their introduction.

Notwithstanding all these difficulties and obstacles, it is a fact that the photo-gelatine process has gained ground sufficiently to indicate a prosperous future, as its products are becoming more widely known and appreciated.

OFFSET PRINTING

By George E. Loder

NO account of the production of a book would be complete without a description of the offset process and its rapid rise to prominence in the book printing industry.

In connection with this subject, however, the seeker for information will find it helpful to read also the articles in this volume on presswork, line and half-tone plate making, and the making and printing of intaglio plates. And by no means should that on lithography be omitted.

Offset printing is a "planographic" process—that is, the printing is done from a flat surface, as distinguished from relief printing which is done from raised surfaces, as type, line cuts, etc., and from intaglio printing, which is done from plates into whose surfaces lines have been cut, such as an engraved business card, an etching or a photogravure.

We often hear of "offset lithography," for the word lithography has been rather loosely applied to all forms of planographic printing, whether the medium used was stone, zinc, or aluminum, all of which substances have been found satisfactory for plain surface printing.

The offset press was designed, however, for the use of either zinc or aluminum plates and has rapidly superseded the older stone, or straight lithographic press. In fact, so rapid has been the advance of offset printing, that after about twenty-five years of development, the ratio of offset presses to those printing from stone is about ten to one. It is obvious that a press, which operates more than twice as fast, uses metal plates which are easier to handle and to store than lithographic stones, and turns out a finished result comparable in almost every way to printing from lithographic stones, must take a prominent place in the printing industry.

Perhaps the most important use for offset printing in the book world is in the actual reproduction of a volume which has already been printed by the usual type printing process. If the original edition has been exhausted and there are no electrotype plates from which to print another, an excellent reproduction can be made by offset, generally at a much lower cost than that of resetting the type and printing from it.

When a book is to be reprinted in this way, the best copy available is taken carefully from its covers; the leaves are flattened out and laid side by side so that several—generally four, eight, or even more—pages may be photographed together.

The best negative is obtained by the "wet plate" method, in which the photographer prepares his own glass plates with the usual sensitive silver solution, and is able, by skillful handling, to equal, and often improve upon, the original pages. For books which do not require the finest results, the less expensive film and paper negatives may be used.

After the negative has been made, it is dried and coated with rubber cement and collodion to give it sufficient body so it can be stripped off the glass and handled easily. It is then cut up, and each page is placed in its proper position on a layout sheet that has already been prepared. This layout is no more than the regulation book press imposition, but it is drawn on transparent paper or glass and shows all the margins and placing of the pages which comprise a form whether there are eight, sixteen, thirty-two or sixty-four pages.

It is then necessary to "opaque out," or cover, any light spots that mar the otherwise black background of the film. The form of pages is then ready to be printed on a zinc, or aluminum plate, whichever may be preferred. These have already been grained, or roughened, to give them a surface that will retain moisture.

The metal plates vary in thickness from .010 to .028 of an inch and in size from 22 by 30 inches to 48 by 65 inches, depending upon the size of the press for which they are intended. They are made sensitive to the action of light by coating them with a solution of bichromate of ammonia and egg albumen. The plate is then placed in a frame which also contains the form or "flat" of page negatives. The frame is locked and a vacuum is used to get an absolutely perfect contact between the two. After an exposure to arc lights for four to eight minutes, the metal plate is removed and covered with a specially prepared greasy ink. It is then placed in a trough for development under water.

The parts of the metal plate which have been in contact with the letters or the design in the original book have been chemically changed by the action of the light, thus leaving those parts of the surface with a hardened layer of bichromate and egg. Since the whole plate was covered with the greasy ink, this has naturally adhered to these parts and they do not wash off. The finished plate therefore shows the design standing out clearly and sharply in black ink on the otherwise unchanged surface of the metal plate.

It is an important characteristic of the planographic plate that it can be "touched up" if any imperfections have occurred and that entirely new work may, if desired, be drawn in. A greasy lithographic ink is used for the purpose, and it may be applied either by pen or brush.

The plate is then ready for its first etching, which is accomplished by a very light application of acid which acts on the surface not covered with the greasy ink. This etching is designed simply to reduce the spots that ought not show up on the plate.

After the second or third etching, the plate is ready to be printed and is clamped firmly around the impression cylinder of the press. As this revolves, the plate is first traversed by a roller distributing the moisture from the water fountain. This water adheres to all the surface excepting the inked lines. Then follows an ink roller distributing the ink from the ink fountain and this ink avoids the moist portions but adheres to the inked lines. The impression of the inked plate is then transferred to a rubber blanket which has been tightly drawn around the second cylinder of the press. This rubber blanket, revolving in turn, actually prints the pages on the sheet of paper, thus producing the printed sheets which are to be bound later in book form.

Naturally the easiest book to reproduce well is one clearly printed from type and which has only simple line cuts. Most of the books that are reprinted are in this class. There are, however, some which have prints of old wood engravings, sometimes of most delicate design and minute detail, and other old books with soiled pages and blurred type. Both of these can be photographed but often only with considerable difficulty and the exercise of much skill on the part of the photographer. Pen sketches, drawings, and often old lithographic prints find their way in front of the lens again and are eventually printed by the fast running offset press.

The reproduction of half-tone prints is extremely difficult, but, when necessary, can be done with amazingly good results. A German process, the so-called "Manul Method of Reproduction," seems to be the best means of obtaining faithful negatives from such prints.

One of the practical advantages of the offset press is that "making ready," which usually takes a long time on a type press, is almost eliminated. The process, therefore, is well adapted to printing, at low cost, even such small runs as 100, 500 or 1000 impressions, while the speed of the press, which is able to produce from 2000 to 3500 impressions per hour, renders it equally valuable for large editions running into the hundred thousands.

The offset plate has not yet attained the lasting qualities of the high grade electrotype, since runs of over 100,000 from one plate are undesirable, but this disadvantage is greatly mitigated by the fact that new plates can be made very speedily and economically from the original negative. Also the plates can be preserved for future runs, for the storage space required is almost negligible. A book of 448 pages, size 6 by 9 inches, would probably be made in fourteen forms of thirty-two pages each, on zinc plates about 42½ by 52 inches, each one being about .014 inch thick. These fourteen plates would take up less storage room than a form of a thirty-two page electrotype plates of like size.

Almost any paper ordinarily used for book printing is suitable for the offset press. Because the rubber blanket, not the metal plate, transfers the design to the paper, it is possible to use rough finished papers. Antique book papers, which are soft and fuzzy, are not suitable because the small particles adhere to the rubber blanket; and a highly coated paper is likewise unsuitable, because it is not made to resist moisture. The papers easiest to run are bonds, ledgers, and the special so-called "offset" stock, which is half-way between an antique and machine finished book paper.

Various kinds of inserts for books are often printed by the offset process, although this is not practical unless there are eight or more pages to be printed at one time. This is because small offset presses are not in general use, and the cost of printing one or two pages on a large press would be nearly as great as that of printing a full form of 32 or more pages.

Maps or illustrations in black or in several colors are very attractive when produced by offset. Tracings or stamped originals can be made and photographed in the same way as type pages; as many as possible are combined on one plate for printing economy. Most of the color plates for map work are drawn by hand on key plates which have been made from the black by means of dusting a proof with chalk and laying this impression down on the clean metal. All tints are made this way, but often solid colors, such as roads, railroad lines, and so forth, are made directly from the photographic negative. Offset color process plates can be prepared for inserts in full color with a most delicate and pleasing effect. They are made in much the same way as photo-engravings, by means of color separation negatives and art work on both negative and plate.

The finished sheets, as they come from the offset press, are in practically the same physical condition as the product of the type press and may be treated in the same way as regards folding, binding, and so forth. Firms using offset presses generally do not attempt to bind books; the flat sheets are delivered to the book binder, just as is the case with the ordinary book printer.

If we could look a few years into the future it is possible we might see an offset press printing book forms from a roll of paper, two sides at a time, at the rate of five or six thousand impressions per hour. Such presses have been built for folder and catalogue work. May they not be used in the future for printing the publisher's big editions?

THE COVER STAMPS

By Philip Becker, Jr.

BOOK stamps are usually cut in a hard brass which is especially made for the purpose. A few are cut in steel because very large editions of the book are expected. The thickness of the brass varies from three-sixteenths of an inch, as used in Boston, to three-eighths of an inch, as used in the Middle West. In New York and Philadelphia, it has always been one-quarter inch thick, and this has become the standard in most localities. Hard brass is used, because, while it is readily workable by machine and with hand-cutting tools, it will stand up under hard usage for many thousands of impressions on book covers.

Until comparatively recent times, very crude and primitive devices were used in making the stamps. The engraver very seldom had more than a pencil sketch to work from, and after transferring this to the brass by pressure, the brass being sized to retain the lead marks, the tedious process was begun of outlining it by hand with a graver and afterward finishing it with a chisel.

But the exacting demands of modern artistic taste, the improvement of scientific methods, and the pressure of competition have effected a complete transformation in the business of making stamps for book covers. A few pencils and gravers, a vise bench, and a grindstone no longer make an engraving establishment. Modern high speed routing machines, machine planers, metal cutting saws, accurate cameras, etching machines, and a competent art department are now necessary for a shop which specializes in the making of cover stamps.

The job starts, naturally, with the drawing, which may be made by the engraver or furnished by the publisher. The drawing, if intended for a one-color stamping, is carefully made in black ink on white paper or drawing board. It may be any size but must be in the right proportion for the cover. If a book is to be stamped in several colors, the design is often painted in the colors on a piece of the cloth to be used, so that the publisher may visualize the completed cover before it is accepted by him. In such a case, black and white tracings must be made and accurately photographed to keep the proper register of colors. This is usually done by the engraving shop, even though it did not design the cover.

The drawing is given to the photographer, who is responsible for the making of practically perfect reproductions of the drawings, as to size. He also prints, from this, negatives on a smooth even piece of brass, covered with a sensitized coating, one plate for each color to be stamped.

The etcher, then, in a succession of "bites," eats down into the brass plate with acid, protecting the face and sides of the design as it progresses. The process up to this point is very similar to that used for zinc etching in the photo-engraving etablishments, with this very important exception—that quarter-inch brass is etched instead of a thin plate of zinc. Brass is an alloy, and difficulties are often encountered because of improper mixing or rolling of the brass when made. In his etching, the etcher does what the most careful hand worker could not accomplish; he produces a practically perfect facsimile of the original drawing in all its artistic freedom. This is very important, because famous artists often draw for book covers, and not to reproduce these drawings exactly would rob the publisher of something that he had paid well to obtain.

Having been etched as deeply as is safe, the plate is then turned over to the router, whose business it is to cut out all the metal between ornaments and lettering to the proper depth. This done, the engraver, who in former years practically dug out the entire plate with his hand tools, comes in to finish the job and correct any slight imperfection that may remain. It is important that the dies should be clear-cut and deep to avoid clogging up in printing, particularly in the plates used for stamping in inks. The experienced and watchful engraver is expected to detect any spots where the etching process has not fully accomplished its purpose. Lettering, especially, should be cut clear, deep, and free from "feather," or ragged edges.

The art department, a necessary part of a modern

book stamp business, originates many of the designs to be made into stamps, and a knowledge of stamping methods is necessary to design them properly. Many times a proposed drawing is impractical because of the color, pattern, or size of the book, and an engraver must be able to advise the customer, or his manufacturing man, that a proposed stamp, even though it can be made very successfully, will not give a successful or proper result when stamped on the book.

Of all the elements that go to make book cover decoration, the lettering is by far the most important. It demands special care, as in some cases it constitutes the entire decoration. In this respect the critical taste of the present day shows itself even more strongly than in the matter of decorative ornamentation, and no amount of ornamentation, whatever its artistic value, can redeem a cover whose lettering is lacking in style, character, or typographical merit of some kind.

The die, when finished, is used by the binder in a stamping press. Color work calls for considerable skill on the part of the stamper, who should be an expert in mixing inks, for a good die will often show poor results if not properly handled. In fact, the success of a book cover depends on three individuals—the artist who designs it, the engraver who cuts it, and the stamper who prints it.

BOOK CLOTHS

By Harold E. Shaw

THE great increase in the number of books produced each year has brought a corresponding development in the use of prepared cloth for the bindings. Previous to the beginning of the nineteenth century, cloth was almost unknown as a material for covering a book. Books were then very costly. They were printed laboriously by hand, on paper also made by hand, and were naturally considered worthy of the most lasting bindings. As the life of a book depends largely on the strength and wearing quality of the covers, such materials as wood, vellum, and leather often reinforced with metal, were generally used.

The nineteenth century saw a great advance in the variety and quantity, if not in the quality, of published books. Improvements in methods and in machinery have progressed side by side with economies in paper making and printing. As the cost of producing the printed sheets became less, a demand arose for a correspondingly cheaper material for bindings. The want was satisfactorily met by the use of cloth, and from the day that it was first used it has become more and more an important factor in book manufacturing.

When so commonplace a binding material as cloth was selected, artists and binders and publishers considered that ornamentation on such a material was almost a waste of time and money. So the libraries of our grandfathers contained rows of gloomy and unattractive books, bound in black cloth stamped in old-fashioned designs, with a back title of lemon gold, and it is only a comparatively few years ago that binding in cloth began to be considered worthy of the attention of the designer and the artist, but since then the demand for a more varied assortment and a wider choice of colors and patterns has been steadily growing.

Let us consider briefly the different kinds of book cloths that are most commonly used today and try to make clear the different fabrics, whose nomenclature is so frequently confused even by binders and publishers.

From their appearance and method of manufacture book cloths fall into two natural divisions, the first being the so-called "solid" colors in which the threads of the cloth are not easily distinguishable. This division contains several grades, the "extra colors," which are the most expensive, the "common colors," and one or two qualities suitable for low-priced books.

The second division consists of the so-called "linens" and "buckrams," in which each thread, with the imperfections and peculiarities of the weaving, is plainly seen and forms a large part of the picturesque effect.

The first black cloth already referred to was a common-color grade, but there are now many colors, though chiefly simple, but pronounced shades, such as browns, blues, greens and reds. These cloths are dyed and sized with a stiffening preparation that also prevents the glue used in attaching them to the cover boards from coming through to the surface. They are less expensive than the extra colors and may be embossed on the surface during the process of manufacture.

The standard width of most book cloths is thirty-eight inches. Cloths are sold by the yard, and the standard number of yards to the roll is forty unless otherwise ordered.

The less expensive of the three qualities of "solid color" cloths is usually furnished in the thirty-six inch width and is made to look as much as possible like the common colors. The strength, however, is inferior.

The ordinary patterns which are in the greatest use today are designated in the trade by letters. Perhaps the most familiar is the "T" pattern, straight parallel ridges or striations, about forty to the inch, and running across the cloth from selvage to selvage. When properly used, these ribs run from top to bottom of a book cover. For this reason it is not economical to use the "T" pattern if the height of the cover is not a multiple of the width of the cloth, as it results in a waste of cloth. This explains why the cost of the book bound in "T" pattern is frequently somewhat higher than the same book bound in another pattern of the same cloth, or in plain or vellum finished cloth.

Another design is the "S" or silk pattern, made up

of finer lines running diagonally across the cloth giving the surface a sheen somewhat resembling silk. Also in ordinary use is a group of patterns composed of small, irregular dots, or points, the finest of which is known as the "C" pattern, a coarser pattern of similar design known as "J," and, coarser still, the "L" which has somewhat the appearance of the coarse grain of a morocco leather. The pattern known as "H" is a simple diamond made by intersecting diagonal lines similar to the ribs of the "T" pattern. Then there are the "BA" and "LW" patterns which resemble the woven appearance of linen and are called "linen weave" patterns. Besides these there are patterns resembling morocco leather and other fancy designs.

Following the increased use of the common cloths, attention was given to the artistic effects which might be obtained by using colored inks and gold on lettering and design, and also to the effects obtained by heating dies and stamping them upon covers made of embossed cloths. This latter process is known in binding as "blanking," or "blind" stamping.

With these advances in the art of cover decoration came the demand for the more delicate tints and richer shades of the colors, and as a result finer colors than could be produced in the common cloths were introduced to meet this demand. These fabrics were called the "extra" colors. They have a solid, smooth enameled surface, more "body" and in every way are firmer and better fabrics. They are more expensive, too; some of them costing from twenty to forty per cent more than the common cloths.

"Extra" cloths are used largely on the better class of books such as special bindings, scientific works, books of reference and holiday volumes, or whenever a fine coloring or better appearance is desired. These cloths are used in the plain finish, which is known as "vellum," and in the "T," "S," "BA," and "LW" patterns. The trained eye can easily recognize extra cloths from the common cloths by the appearance of the surface, but anyone may readily distinguish them by the appearance of the back, which in the common colors is the same color as the face. In the extras the back of the cloth is whitish.

Of the second division of cloths, in which the appearance of the threads becomes a part of the effect, there are first the "linen" cloths. The name "linen" applied to this group is really a misnomer, for many laymen think that such cloths have flax as a foundation and are therefore genuine linens. This is not so, for there is but one genuine linen book cloth to be had, and that is a coarse, irregularly woven cloth, dyed in dull colors, and manufactured by a foreign house. It is quite expensive and hence is seldom used.

The chief characteristics of the "linen" cloths are that the coloring matter fills the interstices, but allows all the knots of the threads to be clearly seen. The irregularities of the weaving, therefore, stand out plainly, and produce, to a certain extent, the appearance of woven linen fabrics.

Linen book cloths are made in three grades and are sold by the yard under special names given to them by the manufacturers. The cheaper qualities are sold as Sterling Linen, Tuxedo Linen or Lintex. The medium quality, which is the one most used, is sold as Rex Vellum, Vellum de Luxe, or Oxford. A still better grade of linen book cloth, somewhat more expensive, sells under the name of Aldine Vellum, Art Vellum, or Linen finish. This latter grade is a very durable, finely woven fabric, extensively used by certain publishers for text-books.

The linen cloths are made principally in the plain, or vellum finish, and in the T and S patterns, but never in any other, the reason for this being the fact that the appearance of the cloth is very little changed by embossing, which can be done with greater effect upon cloths with solid colors. The linen cloths are well adapted for school books which are constantly handled, as their construction shows the wear less than do the solid-color cloths.

The buckrams might be classed with the linens, as that is what, in fact, they are. Linen cloth observed through a microscope which magnifies the threads to a coarseness of about forty to the inch gives us the exact appearance of the buckram, which is a heavy, strong cloth well adapted to large books, and which furnishes the most durable binding of all the book cloths. The colors of the buckrams correspond closely with those of the linens. They are also sold under trade names given them by the manufacturers, such as Art Canvas and Record Buckram, Art Buckram and Library Buckram.

Buckrams are sometimes embossed to imitate in part the appearance of an irregularly woven fabric called "crash."

In describing the various cloths, only those of American manufacture have been considered. There are English cloths which correspond to nearly all of these fabrics, but they are little used in America on account of the delay in importing them and because of the duty, which makes the price here higher than for corresponding grades of domestic manufacture.

BOOK LEATHERS

By Frederick N. Moore

THERE are three animals which give us most of the leather used for bookbinding—sheep, cow and goat. These are divided into several varieties and tannages and we will consider them in order.

Sheep are divided into two kinds, the wool sheep and the hair sheep. The wool sheep are not the best for leather as they are grown principally for the wool and a good wool-bearing animal usually has a poor skin. Wool sheepskins are customarily put through either the sumac or bark process of tanning. Sumac tanned sheepskins would be excellent for bookbinding but are little used. It is a strong tannage, takes a good color and is very long lived. Sumac comes from Sicily and is imported into this country in large quantities. Sumac tanned sheepskins are used mostly for shoes though quite a little for embossed work for bookbinding. Skivers, which are only the grain of the skin,—i.e., the outside part of the skin separated by splitting from the flesh side—are usually tanned by sumac, though they are also tanned by the bark process especially when they are to be used for pass-books, etc. The flesh side is put into chamois or glove leather.

Bark tanned sheepskin is used for law books which makes it one of the most common leathers in the book-binding trade. It does not wear very well, however, as it is very soft, and in a few years crumbles and breaks off whenever touched. These skins really have no oil in them. When it is possible, therefore, it is a good idea to give the leather a little oil or vaseline. Neat's-foot, castor or sweet oil are the best oils.

Sheepskin would be much more durable if it were tanned by the sumac process, especially if care were taken to make it acid free. Most of our books bound before 1875 were tanned that way and are in spendid physical condition as compared with those bound since that time.

The hair sheep is a peculiar animal. We have none around here and if we did we would probably call it a goat. It is found in mountainous places and the principal countries from which it comes are India, China, South America and Africa,—the very best coming from India and South America. The larger part of hair skins is tanned by the chrome method and called *cabretta*, being used both in black and colors for shoe work. A hair sheepskin has a fine grain and a strong fiber, and is very valuable. Chrome tanned leathers are never used for bookbinding because they are soft, will not take grain like morocco, and usually contain too much oil.

In using cowhide for bookbinding, either the grain side is used and is called a "buffing," or else it is split a little thicker and called "cowhide"; this explains the wide difference in cost between buffings and bookbinder's cowhide. Cowhides in general are split into three skins, the grain, the middle split and the bottom split. When done this way the grain is used for bookbinding, the second split for patent leather, or buffing, the third for any old finish that will help to increase its selling price.

Of course there are other ways of treating cowhides. In some, the hide is finished as a whole without splitting, but this is very seldom; others make just one splitting, and still others three, leaving four separate skins. The only trouble with buffing or cowhide is that they break easily and in a few years crumble to pieces. This is because the fiber has been damaged by splitting—weakening the hide fiber greatly. Then, too quick tannages are often used, and they are very seldom made acid free.

Calf is, of course, the young cow and as the skin is not old, it has a finer, stronger grain and will give much longer wear. The only trouble with calfskin is that bookbinders generally use a poor tannage, and to get the light colors the skins have to be bleached which also takes from its strength. If it were possible to use calfskin tanned by the same chrome process as is used in our shoes you would hear no longer the cry that calfskin bound books give out quickly. Calfskins, however, though beautiful in grain and color, have a tender grain which scars and scuffs easily.

Goat skins are tanned in the various tannages.

Chrome-tanned goat skin is probably the best leather made and is manufactured in the greatest quantity. It is used wholly for shoe work. Of vegetable-tanned goat skins, the India goat is the principal one and the best of all for bookbinding.

India sheep and goat skins, such as are used for bookbinding, come from India already tanned. Natives here, there and everywhere, as they kill their sheep and goats, dry the skins in the sun with any preservative, such as salt, as they may have. These skins finally reach the tanneries where they are tanned by the old native tannage which has been in use no one knows how long. Each tanner has a little different method, but in the main features they are all the same. The skins come to this country in large bales containing different grades which range from the very finest to the very worst. These skins could tell quite a history. Here is a small skin, measuring about one square foot. The texture is very fine and is an excellent leather. There is a most pitiful skin. It is probably from an unborn animal or one just born, and the poor little fellow starved to death. You can see where the ribs show right through the skin, every rib and the backbone plainly marked with black streaks.

This large, heavy skin is from an old bull goat, which has seen many years of fighting. His skin is wrinkled with age and hardened with exposure. From them one can read the history of each hide. Some are battle-scarred, some are from animals that died from disease. Here we have a fine, plump skin, one from a well fed, well cared-for animal, which was killed in its prime for food and this is the kind of skin a bookbinder ought to use but unfortunately does not always get.

Few of us ever stop to think of the number of animals that are slaughtered every year. It is easy to speak of "ten dozen skins" but it seems another thing if instead of the "ten dozen" we should say 120 sheep, or instead of "making 300 dozen skins a day," say, 3600 sheep or goats, and when multiplied by 300 days it can easily be seen what an immense number of animals is necessary to keep bookbinders and shoe men busy.

India sheepskin is very similar to the India goat, and as we said before, many people call it a goat. It is very strong, does not rub or scar easily and is one of the most valuable for bookbinding.

Tanned skins always have more or less loose flesh on them. This must be taken off first. Shaving skins used to be done wholly by hand, and while it was profitable, it was a back-breaking operation. Now the wet skin is put into a machine arranged so that a sharp, many-knifed roller turns rapidly while the operator slides the skins in and out, as he finds necessary, and varies the pressure on the knife.

As all skins are more or less dirty and usually retain some of the tanning material, they have to be carefully washed.

There are three different methods of coloring skins. The most usual is to put 20 or 40 dozen skins into a hollow wheel, or drum, fitted with small pins which, as the wheel turns, separate the skins from each other so that each skin gets its proper share of color. Coloring matter, heated to the temperature necessary to penetrate the skins, is added. Sometimes it is necessary to put in a "bottom" color first, then add another and then another to produce the desired results. This method colors the skin on both sides.

If the leather is to be acid free, care must be taken not to use acids that would injure the leather in any way. Sulphuric acid is the enemy of durable book leathers and should not be used in any form or manner.

Another way of coloring is a hand process by which the best skins are spread upon a table and a foundation color is rubbed in by a swab or brush. This is followed by more coloring material until the same result is obtained as by coloring in the wheel, but at a much larger expense.

Another way is coloring to obtain marble effects. The wet skins are rolled up into a round ball, each skin carefully arranged so that no very large part of a skin is hidden in the folds. This ball is then dropped into the color which, of course, takes only on the edges, the folds keeping parts untouched. This produces a beautiful coloring or marble effect, and is somewhat similar to the "treeing" of calf.

The skins are then taken from the coloring wheel and "put out" on a low, slanting bench. Men with glass slickers go over the skins pressing out all the surplus coloring material and smoothing the skins out until they are perfectly flat. This is a very necessary operation, for if the wrinkles are not worked out at this time they never will be. Machines also do this work and have largely superseded hand work.

There are two ways of drying skins. One to hang them up in a hot room on nails, the other to tack them out on boards. The latter is the usual way for bookbinder's use, as the stretch must all be taken out, and the skins left perfectly flat. In heat of about 90 to 100 degrees the skins take about one day to dry properly. Sheepskins cannot be dried in heat, as they would become brittle.

From this point, methods differ as to finishing. They depend upon what color, finish and other features are wanted.

As it is desirable to have some leathers very soft, which is exactly opposite to book leather, we have what we call a "staking machine" which grasps the skin and, as the operator holds it, lets go very gradually, thus stretching the skin at all points, until the leather is nice and soft.

Oftentimes it is necessary to give the skin a little more color to fill in the pores, especially if the stock must be brighter. This is of real importance to bookbinders, for the same material which we put on our leathers at this time is what every binder should use as a wash for his books. Boil a little flaxseed in water, then add a little milk to this mixture and you will have a fine effect if this is put on the books before they are pressed out. Be sure to allow full time for drying.

There are several ways of putting a "grain" or embossed finish on leathers—expensive ones by hand processes and cheaper by running the skins through steel rolls. Very excellent effects may be given to leathers in this latter manner, but it is apt to injure the fiber and so should not be used for fine books.

Finally let it be said that the rule every bookbinder ought to follow is to select the best possible stock, and then be sure that no acid has been used in the tanning.

A really good leather is the best material there is for a book cover. But it must be really good.

LEATHER SUBSTITUTES

By R. A. Applegate

ANCIENT books were usually bound in leather and the finest of leather, the very "top of the hide," was used in the binding as befitted the covers of such splendid works of art. Many of these ancient books have come down to us in a fine state of preservation.

In recent years, however, because of the increasing quantities of books, some of which run into editions of hundreds of thousands of copies, the cost of leather for binding has become prohibitive. In fact there have not been enough hides to supply the demand. Therefore, there was a real necessity, in the bookbinding and publishing industries, for a satisfactory substitute for leather. There are several kinds of these so-called "substitute leathers" one of which is "Fabrikoid."

The base of Fabrikoid is a cotton fabric, the weight and weave varying according to the way in which the finished product is to be used. Upon this woven cotton fabric foundation are applied successive coatings of pyroxylin, which are carefully spread upon and firmly anchored into the cloth until a protective and impermeable film of appreciable thickness has been built up.

Pyroxylin is really cotton, but it is cotton that has

been changed chemically by dissolving it with various solvents until it is an adhesive jelly, of many peculiar characteristics. Pigments are ground into this jelly to give it the desired color. When the colored jelly is forced into the woven cotton fabric base it becomes a tough, flexible film which when dry is practically inseparable from the fabric. In other words, the base being woven cotton and the solution which is spread upon it also being cotton, these like products, having a natural affinity for each other, merge into one homogeneous mass. This gives to the finished material a high degree of resistance to all the ordinary results of changing climate, wear and age.

As pyroxylin is insoluble in water, the fabric to which it has been applied becomes completely waterproof. It is also one of the most stable compounds known. Nothing likely to come in contact with it in the ordinary life of a book can stain or change it. Soap, for instance, has no effect on it, so that both soap and water, the commonest of all cleansing combinations, can be freely used in renovation. It does not harden with age or in long service but always retains its flexibility and vitality and its grip upon the fabric of which it is a part. Nor does it flake off or disintegrate, or lose its richness and luster.

In coloring pyroxylin, fluid dyes are avoided almost entirely and solid pigments, which are natural earth minerals, are used in practically all cases. These natural pigments are non-deteriorating, insoluble and light-proof. They are distributed throughout the pyroxylin coating in a condition of such fineness that they saturate it completely, thus embedding the color so firmly that it can not become scuffed or worn under ordinary conditions of service.

The pyroxylin surface of Fabrikoid is also absolutely impervious. While it is possible that dust, grease or other foreign matter may lodge upon it, nothing can find passage into the material itself, for there are no pores through which it can pass or in which it can lodge and defy removal. This means that such material makes an absolutely sanitary book covering. In fact it can actually be sterilized with carbolic acid, bichloride of mercury, or Dakin solution. It is immune also to the attacks of insects, rodents and the well known destructive "bookworm."

The surface of Fabrikoid may be finished with a grain similar to that of real leather. This is obtained by passing the material between hot steam rollers which emboss the surface, and there is a great variety in the designs which may be used in this way.

"Superfinish" is a recently developed process which has vastly increased the artistic uses of Fabrikoid. The process consists of die-embossing the covers and coloring them by the air brush method. It is particularly well adapted for covers of catalogs, advertising booklets, college annuals, subscription sets and other special volumes. So many excellent covers of this type have been made and have had such nation-wide distribution that most of us are familiar with their appearance.

Due to the many angles which must be considered in producing covers by the superfinish process, only binders thoroughly familiar with its method should attempt the work, and to help and instruct these the manufacturers maintain a large and experienced service department.

In spite of all the advantages of pyroxylin-coated fabrics, there have been until recently two technical disadvantages. While these have not been sufficiently vital to outweigh the many advantages inherent in the material, they have nevertheless caused the bookbinders of the country some inconvenience.

Pyroxylin-coated material, because of its extremely tough and non-porous surface, is difficult to make adhere to the paper "end sheets" of a book without first washing the turned-in edges of the material with a solvent to lessen the resistance of the pyroxylin. This same resistant surface often caused difficulty in stamping with printing ink, genuine gold leaf "alchemic" gold, or other gold substitutes without first sizing the cover with albumen.

In June, 1925, the Bookbinders' Guild of New York City placed these problems before the manufacturers of Fabrikoid, and for more than two years their chemists, co-operating with men skilled in the technicalities of bookbinding, have worked to solve them. The result is what is known as "Book-Kraft Fabrikoid."

Samples of this new material were recently submitted to the members of the Guild for experimental purposes, and in a short time they reported almost unanimously that it had surpassed their expectations. In addition, the two technical difficulties which had formerly caused so much trouble for the publisher, binder and printer were entirely eliminated. The perfected fabric is washable, waterproof, wear-resisting, scuff and vermin-proof; it can be glued or pasted to end sheets with any of the ordinary adhesives used in bindery practice and without the added operation of washing the turned-in edges with a solvent solution; it can be stamped with genuine gold leaf, alchemic gold or any of the gold substitutes without sizing; it can be written or printed on with ordinary ink.

THE BINDING

By E. W. Palmer

THE reader has doubtless observed, from the article on presswork, that book pages are printed on paper in forms of sixteen, thirty-two, sixty-four and often one hundred and twenty-eight pages. Obviously it follows that some method of reducing these large printed sheets to convenient workable units for binding must be followed.

In laying out a book for printing, the printer selects the "imposition" (or arrangement of the printed pages) best suited to the size of finished book, the number of pages in the book and the number of pages which the thickness and character of paper will permit the binder to fold into individual sections, or "signatures."

From the printing press the printed sheets, in orderly piles, go to folding machines which are capable of folding a great variety of impositions. Here, one by one, the printed sheets are propelled by mechanical fingers into the machines which cut the large sheets and reduce them, by folding the sections into folded signatures. These may consist of eight, sixteen, twenty-four or thirty-two pages each. After inspection, these sections are bundled under pressure and passed along for the operations of pasting, reinforcing and gathering.

Pasting, the term denoting the affixing of separately printed illustrations into the sections or signatures, is not, as most people believe, accomplished after the binding, nor by inserting each successive insert one at a time into the individual book. Automatically-fed machines firmly paste these insert leaves onto the *outside* of sections. All that go *inside* of a section must be pasted in by handwork. Girls become very adept in this work. Each insert leaf is handled by itself, and as many as ten thousand or more of the same insert may be pasted into an equal number of the same signature by one girl in a day's time. And this proceeds until all the insert leaves are properly placed in all the sections.

Meanwhile the end-papers, which later are made to adhere to the inner side of the cover, are prepared and pasted to the first and last sections of the book. Likewise any strengthening features, such as adding concealed muslin joints or whipstitching to strengthen the end sections or those that have a good many pastings, will be attended to. There are many types of inserts and of reinforcements, each requiring a particular method of treatment.

The signatures are now ready for gathering, which is the operation of bringing all the sections of the book, until now in separate units of folded pages, into their proper sequence, thus constituting a complete book. Small editions are often assembled, or gathered by girl

operatives.   This is called hand gathering.   In plants
where large editions are printed, the gathering is performed today by huge machines, which consist of thirty
pockets, or magazines, and a traveling conveyor.   As the
machine operates, one copy of all of its sections is
dropped simultaneously onto the conveyor which travels
along until completely gathered books emerge at the
delivery end, at the rate of from ten thousand to thirty
thousand copies a day.

The gathered books must next be sewn so that several
sections will be held together and provide for a firm but
flexible binding.   There are many types of sewing
machines, but all operate on a similar principle.   A section is laid over an arm of the machine, which carries it
into the machine mechanism, where rapidly moving
needles, operating at marvelous speed, sew each section
to the next with strong thread.   Several books emerge
from the machine in a solid block and are separated by
cutting the thread between each two books.   The lock-
stitch prevents the threads from unravelling.

Books of the better sort, and those of difficult make-
up, are often "collated" before sewing to prevent dupli-
cation of sections or more serious errors.   Collating
consists of looking through each individual book and
checking the page sequence, the placing of inserts, the
reinforcements, etc.

As book papers vary in bulk and a "swell" is caused
at the back by reason of the thickness of the two threads
added to each section, it is now necessary to "smash"

or "nip" the books to secure uniform thickness and to avoid a wedge shape. Uniform thickness is essential so the covers, which are being made while the books are being sewed, shall properly fit when sheets and cover are put together. Smashing is accompanied by squeezing the sewed books, either singly or in groups of two or more depending on their bulk, between the upper and lower jaws of a huge power-driven compressor. Nipping consists of squeezing along the back or binding edge only, and is usually employed for books printed on hard finished papers, especially school books.

Trimming, or cutting the three edges is the next operation. Power machines with one, two or three knives are used and books are trimmed either singly or in units of two or more as their bulk and the character of the paper permit. A continuously operating book trimmer, in which all three edges are trimmed simultaneously at the rate of from twenty to thirty-five thousand books each day, is a most interesting machine. For rough-cut edges the same machines are employed, but only the top edge is actually cut smooth, while the side and "foot" edges are trimmed only just enough to open the folded edges of the sections. Following this partial trimming the books are fed with the side and foot edges against an abrasive disk, or wheel, which roughens these edges, simulating the old time deckle edges. Books that are to have rounded corners are again cut after the edge trimming, this time with a circular corner knife.

Treatment of the edges of a book takes many forms,

perhaps the most familiar is the gilded edges, top or full. Books which have been trimmed, are carefully arranged in a row in a gilder's press, or clamp, and the edges are scraped and sandpapered until absolutely smooth. Then a filler is applied, the edges are sized with a liquid albumen mixture, and genuine gold in leaves 3⅜ x 3⅞ inches is laid on by hand, each leaf overlapping the next a trifle. After drying, the gold covered edges are burnished by means of an agate or bloodstone tool in the hands of an experienced gilder. The books are then removed from press and separated.

Marbling, which produces the varied colored edges for sets of reference books and encyclopædias, is obtained by dipping the edges in a vat, on the surface of which has been spattered and waved, or combed, water colors in any desired pattern and combination of colors.

Colored edges, showing one solid color, are obtained by sponge or brush coloring, using aniline, or pulp coloring. Solid and sprinkled effects are also secured today by means of air brush sprays.

Sprinkled, or speckled edges are obtained by rubbing a stiff brush saturated with pulp color over a coarse mesh wire screen held above the book edges while the books are laid out on a table, back edge on table, other three edges facing upward.

Following the edge treatment, a coating of flexible glue is applied the full width and length of the back edge. While the glue is still soft but not sticky, the books are fed, one at a time, into a machine that grips it between two sharp steel jaws about ⅛ inch from the back edge and by means of a concave steel shaping-iron imparts the rounded shape to the back and sets up the ridges which appear along the back edge on both sides against which the cover boards are to fit. This rounding and backing, as it is called, shapes the book and prepares it to receive cover properly, to open easily, and to lie flat when opened.

As a book would lack strength and durability if held together merely by thread and glue, it is necessary to reinforce the back. In ordinary bindings this consists of a thorough gluing and the application of a piece of coarse crash, or muslin, which projects over either side of the back edge about an inch, and nearly to the top and bottom edges of the book. Over the crash goes another gluing and on top a piece of firm, strong paper the length and width of the book back.

In the case of heavy books and school books it is customary to affix two layers of crash instead of one; one of these being a fine mesh and the other a coarser mesh.

Headbands, the little ornamental pieces of book cloth, cotton or silk in variegated colors, that appear at the top and bottom edges of the backbone, or shelf-back, are added during this reinforcing operation, which is termed "lining-up."

Until recent years it was necessary to do lining-up and headbanding by hand. Today there are several ingenious machines which accomplish the same results at less cost, at far greater speed and with equal quality of the product.

Meanwhile the various operations incident to the production of the cover for the book have been progressing steadily.

Book cloths, substitute leathers and other cover fabrics are manufactured in rolls, from 36 to 50 inches wide and from 40 to 500 yards in length. The modern bindery employs slitting and winding machines for preparing these fabrics for cover-making machines, or for hand production.

The board used on the sides of the book for stiffening the cover is obtainable in a great variety of qualities, thicknesses and sizes. Here again machines are employed to transform the raw material into units to satisfy the cavernous maw of machines that produce the finished covers.

Cover-making machines which hold cloth in rolls of the proper width, piles of cover boards, and back-lining paper for strengthening the shelf-back of the book, operate to the tune of sixteen to twenty thousand finished covers a day and are now common factors in binderies.

Different types of machines, both hand and machine fed, will produce in smaller quantities similar and other types of covers, including semi-flexible and parti-cloth, or leather covers.

For round or square cornered covers in flexible leather, artificial leather, or cloth, we must resort to handwork, in combination with machines that do the gluing, making round corners.

Embellishing the covers by means of ink, real gold or gold substitutes is a fascinating operation to watch. Inking presses automatically feeding their own covers can produce eighteen thousand perfectly inked covers a day, and contribute their share to our low cost popular novels and moderately priced school books. Huge embossing and stamping presses, with attachments which feed gold or artificial gold ribbons while the operator inserts and removes the covers, produce an endless variety of finished covers. Still larger embossing presses that appear capable of handling sheets of steel, turn a plain, unattractive cover or piece of material into an article of beauty and long life. Here we find girls cutting and laying sheets of real gold on covers preparatory to the slower and more difficult operation of stamping delicate fabrics and leathers, while others remove, by careful brushing and rubbing, the surplus gold or metal particles.

The cover and the book are now ready to be combined. Again machines are employed to shape the backbone of each cover by passing the covers over a heated shaping iron in order that no unsightly bulges or wrinkles may spoil the appearance of the product. Likewise machines combine book and cover, feeding covers from a magazine while the book is fed in by hand and removed in the same manner when safely encased in the cover.

The still damp book must next be laid between wooden pressing boards, each having metal edgings that project over the edge of the boards. This sets the book firmly in the cover at the back or binding edge, and creates the little "valleys" that are found on both sides of the cover. The boards with the books between are then put in a press, where they remain until the books are dry.

After drying from six to twelve hours, the presses, or clamps, are opened, the books carefully inspected, encased in plain or printed jackets or other wrapping, and are then ready for shipment.

This, briefly, is the story of modern "edition binding." A thousand digressions might be made to amplify the operations or explain the details of the many varieties of binding encountered in any bindery, but that would provide subject matter for a volume in itself.

SPECIAL BINDINGS

By Henry Blackwell

MUCH has been written about the art of special binding, and many lengthy treatises have been written on the various methods of early and modern "extra," or fine binders. It will be my province to describe the stages through which a book passes, from the time it is received in the bindery until it is shipped out of the establishment. I will take for my subject a rare old book that is to be rebound in a half-levant morocco binding. In a good shop, all books, no matter what the binding is to be, are treated alike in regard to workmanship, care, and materials. If a binder puts his name in the completed book, it is a sign that the book has been to the best of his ability, honestly and well bound.

When the customer brings the book to the binder, the style of binding, color of the leather, amount and kind of ornamentation, and all the other details are determined upon and entered carefully in a numbered order book, and the number of the order is marked in pencil on an inside leaf of the book itself, so that the original instructions may be referred to from time to time. This number is usually left in the book after it has been finished and delivered to the owner, and not infrequently has been the means of identifying a lost or stolen volume.

The book is then given to the first operator, usually a girl, who removes the cover, if there is any, and takes the book apart, separating carefully each of the "signatures," or sections, and removing the threads of the old binding. If any of the pages are loose, they are pasted neatly in their proper places and the "insert plates" (illustrations, maps, etc.), which had been printed separately from the text and pasted in the volume, are examined to make sure that they are firmly fixed. Another operator goes over the entire volume and cleans any of the pages that have become soiled.

The book is then prepared for the sewing by a man who hammers the back until it is flat and all the edges of the signatures lie evenly. He then divides it into sections of half a dozen or more signatures, places each of these between smooth wooden boards, and puts the whole into an upright iron press, in which it is subjected to a great pressure, and where it ought to remain over night in order to make it entirely flat and solid. A better way of pressing a book at this stage of the operation is to pass it several times through a rolling machine, which is made for this special purpose with two heavy iron rollers, say twenty inches long and ten inches in diameter.

These machines are seldom used in America, but are invariably found in the equipment of binders' workshops abroad, which is perhaps one reason why English books are so solidly bound.

Following the pressing, or the rolling, the book is placed, back uppermost, in another press, something like a wooden vise. By means of a handsaw, several cuts, just deep enough to cut entirely through the fold of each signature, are made across the back of the book. Seven of these saw marks are usually made, the five in the middle being for the cords on which the book is sewed, and the two at the ends for threads which help to make the sewing more secure. If the book is to have a binding with raised bands across the back, no actual cuts are made, the back being simply scratched to guide the girl in sewing, so that the heavy twine on which she sews will stand out on the back, forcing the leather up in the five middle places and forming the raised bands.

After it has been sawed, or scratched, the book goes to a girl who collates it—that is, examines it thoroughly, signature by signature, and makes sure that everything is in its right place. If the volume is old or especially valuable, it is gone over page by page. The first and last signatures are then whipstitched, or sewed over and over along the back edges, and then put in their places.

The book is then sewn on a "sewing frame." This is a small wooden table about twelve by eighteen inches, with legs only one inch high. At two corners there are upright wooden screws, some fifteen inches long with movable collars which support a crosspiece. To this crosspiece are fastened three stout cords, their other ends being attached to the table. The position of these cords is regulated to fit the saw marks on the back of the book, then they are tightened by means of the screw collars. The sections of the book are placed against these cords, one by one, and the threads passed through the saw cuts and outside the cords, thus sewing them firmly to the back of the book. When several books of the same size are being bound at one time, the operator goes right on sewing book after book, one signature after the other, until she has finished a pile of books a foot or more high. When the sewing is finished the cords are cut so as to leave a free end of an inch and a half on each side of the book, and to these ends are fastened the boards, as described later.

Linen or silk thread is used in sewing, the heaviness of which depends upon the size of the book and the thickness of the paper of the book. If the book has many single leaves, or illustrations, it is sometimes necessary to whipstitch each signature before sewing.

The book, or the pile of books, then passes to the "forwarder," who "draws off" or separates each book from the others in the pile, and again hammers the book, to flatten out any "swell" which may be present after the sewing. He pastes, or "tacks," the first and last whipstitched signatures to the signatures next them, this pasting being only, say, an eighth of an inch wide along the back edge.

The stock is then chosen for the "end papers," usually matching closely the paper of the book. They are cut a little larger than the paper page of the book, and pasted along the edge to the outside and whip-stitched signatures. Marble paper in suitable harmony or contrast with the leather to be used on the book is selected for lining the inside of the covers cut to the same size as the "end papers," and pasted to them, after having been folded so that the colored sides come face to face.

When all this pasting has dried thoroughly, the back of the book is covered with a thin coating of glue, to preserve its shape and, while the back is quite flat, the front edges of the leaves are trimmed off evenly in a cutting machine. If this edge is to be gilded, special care is taken to have the edges cut smoothly.

The back is then "rounded" by use of a hammer; if the book is to be a "flat back" one, the rounding is very slight. It is necessary even in the case of a flat back book to round it somewhat so that it will retain its shape when the finished book is placed on the shelf. After the round-ing, the top, or "head," and the bottom, or "tail," of the book are trimmed evenly in the cutting machine.

The book is ready for the gilder, who places it, with the edge which is to be gilded uppermost, in a press. This edge is covered with red chalk, which shows all the uneven places, which are then scraped with a steel scraper. This operation is repeated until the edge is very smooth, when it is treated with a sizing made of white of egg and water, which is to hold the gold leaf to the edges of the leaves. The gold leaf is laid on the still wet edge, and when slightly dry is covered with a sheet of paper and rubbed down with a burnisher, and when entirely dry is burnished again with a smooth piece of agate or bloodstone.

The boards, pieces of strong and durable binders' "boards" made of paper or tarred rope, are selected and cut to fit the book, extending about one-eighth of an inch over the head, tail, and front edges of the leaves. Each of the cords, on which the book has been sewed, is moistened with paste, and put through two holes which are punched side by side in the board and within a quarter of an inch of the inside edge. The cord is carried down through one hole, and up through the other, and the remaining end is cut off and hammered down smooth where it stays firmly fastened by the paste. This is called "lacing on the boards" and when finished makes, so far as strength is concerned, the cover-boards and the inside of the book practically one piece. The book is given another long pressing.

The coverer then takes the volume. He first wraps the edges with paper to keep them clean and then puts on the headbands. These are either sewn directly on to the book or may be bought ready-made, when they are put on with glue.

The back is covered with a strip of coarsely woven crash lined with several pieces of paper. This is glued to the back to make it hard and solid and to prevent it from cracking, or "breaking," when the book is opened.

The leather is then cut out for the corners and for the back, in the latter case allowance being made for its extension over and on to the boards to the proper distance. The back lining is trimmed off to the top of the headbands, and the leather is pasted on the rough side in position and turned in at the "head" and "tail" of the back. The five raised bands are then "pinched up" and the whole back is polished, or "crushed," with a hot polisher until the leather is smoothed down to the desired surface.

In decorating the cover, or "tooling" it, as it is called, the design is first pressed into the leather of the back with heated tools. These designs, appearing "blank," or sunken, in the leather, are washed over with a thin coat of paste and water, followed by a sizing of albumen, and finally with vaseline, to make the gold stick. Gold leaf is laid over the "blank" designs and the same heated tools used to press the gold into the leather. As many as three layers of gold are frequently put on in this way until the design is full and clear. The waste edges of the pieces of gold leaf are removed with a piece of soft rubber and the whole back washed with benzine to remove the grease of the vaseline and that of the natural leather.

The part of the leather which projects over the sides is pasted to the boards, trimmed off straight, and pared down until the edges are very thin. Another piece of plain paper is then cut out and pasted on the board, covering it right up to the edges of the leather. This makes the side board and the leather even in height and prevents the outside marbled paper from showing ridges made by the edges of the leather.

When the outside has dried, a piece of paper is pasted on the inside of each board. This paper has a tendency to shrink a little and to warp the boards, so that they will hold tightly to the inside of the book. If this paper were not put on the inside of the covers, the marbled paper on the outside might cause the boards to warp away from the book itself.

The end papers are then pasted down on to the board, and when thoroughly dry all the leather along the inside and the outside edges of the cover sides is carefully washed and polished with an iron polisher. The book is then placed between plates made of steel, either nickel or silver plated, and placed in the press to remain a day or two, after which the back is polished again and the sides are finished with gilt lines along the edges of the leather next to the marbled paper. Then the book is finally inspected, a silk marker inserted, and the volume is done and ready for delivery.

LIBRARY BINDING

By Frank M. Barnard

THE so-called "library binding" has been developed as a distinct branch of bookbinding because of the increase in the circulation of books by public and semi-public libraries, and because of the general use of free text-books in the public schools. Every year these agencies have a large number of volumes which must either be replaced or rebound, and for the major portion the latter procedure has been found to be the more desirable.

Binderies devoted exclusively to rebinding are of quite recent origin; most of them are less than fifteen years old and few go back twenty-five years. Before then, librarians usually gave their orders for rebinding to any binder who would take them. The work was looked upon as undesirable from a trade standpoint—something in the nature of a cheap repair job to be done at odd times by the least expensive help in the shop and with indifferent materials.

Today the library bindery is an institution, with trade customs, methods of procedure, specialized machinery, selected stock, and trained craftsmen, all distinctly its own. The United States Census Bureau has recognized this by giving the library bindery a place distinct from other branches of bookbinding in the 1925 statistical reports of the printing and binding trades.

The first efforts toward improving library binding were made in an English bindery, whose proprietor was later induced by a group of American librarians to establish a branch in this country.

The American Library Association also had a part in improving library binding by gathering data on methods and materials, and placing its findings before both librarians and the binding trade. In the year 1922, the activities of the committee in charge included a meeting with a group of library binders affiliated with the organization known as the Employing Bookbinders of America, at which time there was formulated and adopted a set of standardized specifications for the rebinding of library books. Such specifications are of course general in character, laying down principles to be followed rather than specifying much detail.

Every type and character of book finds its way with greater or less frequency into the library bindery, and they fall into three general classes:

1. The rebinding of an ordinary volume of fiction, or a school text-book.

2. The binding of periodicals, or newspapers, into volumes for convenient reference use.

3. The reconstruction of the binding of new books just issued by a publisher and before they have been used at all.

Ordinary books of fiction are usually received in lots of from fifty to one thousand or even more. Shipments from many libraries often arrive at the same time and are put into work simultaneously. Hardly any two volumes are alike, and all must be marked for identification, first as to ownership and second to indicate the binding desired.

Each book is taken apart in the "pulling department" and here is determined whether the condition of the book renders it suitable for rebinding. If it is, a page collation is made, the book removed from its cover, which is usually thrown away, or if in very good condition, may be filed for use. The fly leaves and advertising sheets go into the discard, dry glue is scraped from the back, and section by section the book is taken to pieces, and the torn leaves mended.

It is then decided in what manner the book is to be resewed and otherwise processed, following which it is "benched," that is the ridge at the back is pounded, pressed, or rolled out.

Sewing is generally the next process. Not more than two per cent of the total volumes are in a condition good enough to warrant sewing again *through* the folds of the signatures. The remainder, constituting almost the entire bulk of library binding, have to be "oversewed," either by machine or by hand.

The preparation of books for sewing through their signature folds calls for a determination of whether they are to be sewed on cords or on tapes. In either case saw cuts are made through the folded backs of the signatures, one cut for each cord and this deep enough fully to receive it; or two saw cuts for each tape, these as shallow as possible—just deep enough to aid somewhat in guiding the passage of the needle in and out of the signature. The use of tapes is usually preferred in library binding, and the linen sewing threads pass over or around the tapes or cords as they are strung taut in the sewing frame, which holds them while the sewing is in progress.

Preparation for oversewing differs from the procedure already described. After a volume has been pounded, the inside of the book is examined to see if the back margins of the type pages are of sufficient width to permit the back folds of the sections to be trimmed off. If they are, the trimming gives the back edge a smooth surface and the application of hot glue then converts the book into a tablet of single leaves, which tablet can be divided into sections of suitable thickness for oversewing. Dividing into sections is accomplished by a "pad-counter" or "sectioning machine." The best thickness for a section is about one-fifth of an inch, which will insure a strong volume with good opening qualities.

When the margins are so narrow that it is not advisable to trim the back of the book as above described, the folds are removed by means of a "book sander" with scarcely any loss of margin. Sanding insures a smooth, even edge and the leaves can then be divided into sections of any desired thickness.

Books that are printed on paper lacking in flexibility

do not open well no matter how they may be sewed, but this trouble can be lessened if the leaves are "flexed," or scored, in a "job backer" which takes the sections one by one, clamping them and then folding to right and to left by hand or, with more speed, by the use of the "scoring machine."

The book, or tablet of leaves, having been divided into uniform sections of suitable thicknesss, is ready for the addition of cloth-jointed end sheets and an inspection to make sure that no sections have been transposed or turned upside down. Then the oversewing is done.

The distinctive feature of this sewing, and one that gives it its name, is the fact that the stitches pass through the *edges* rather than through the *folds* of the successive sections, and hence must sew *over* the backs of the sections rather than *through* them. Oversewing requires a much greater number of stitches than regular sewing, and the stitches are placed where the paper is soundest in its structure; hence it gives the book unusual strength.

The "oversewing machine" will oversew every type of book in a ratio of about ten to one as compared with handwork.

Now another inspection, end papers are pasted, or tipped on as required, and the book is passed to the machine that cuts or trims its edges, called a cutting machine or book trimmer. Then if colored or sprinkled edges are wanted, the freshly cut edges are sprayed by an air brush.

When the glue has been well brushed in and has

properly set, the rounding of the back of the book, producing the concave shape of the fore-edge, is accomplished either in the old hand style by means of a hammer, or, and preferably, by the use of a rounding machine.

Lining comes next—a twilled sateen, or a canton flannel with the nap side to the book being used for the purpose. The lining strips are nearly as long as the book and are wide enough to extend around the back and at least an inch on each side. Wheat flour paste is used to attach them. When the freshly lined books have dried then comes the operation of backing. Some binders back their books before lining them, but it is now generally conceded that the book is stronger if lined first.

Backing has for its purpose the formation of such a shape along each edge of the back as will produce a groove suitable for receiving the cover-boards and at the same time permit of neat and convenient joint, or hinge. If the board is fitted closely into its corresponding groove, the joint is spoken of as a "close joint," but if the board is placed some distance away the resulting joint is called a "French joint." This latter is desirable whenever a heavy or stiff material is used for covering purposes.

Backing is usually accomplished by means of a "roller backer." This machine has a pair of powerful jaws to hold the book so that its sewed back projects slightly beyond the jaws. A heavy concave roller then moves back and forth over the projecting back until the back is round and a pair of grooves have been formed.

The jaws of the roller backer are controlled by the foot, and the roller is worked by hand. This process is the most laborious part of library binding. While all other principal operations can be done by power-driven machines, no one has yet devised a means of operating the roller backer by power, due probably to the fact that considerable judgment must be exercised in setting the machine for each successive book.

The rounding and backing of the book usually leaves the end sheets slightly projecting at the fore-edge, and the next operation is therefore the trimming off of such projections so that the end sheets shall be even with the leaves of the book. This may be done with scissors, but is preferably accomplished by means of an "end sheet trimmer," another special machine.

The book is now ready for its covers, the stiff portion of which is made of binders' board, a strong cardboard manufactured from old wrapping paper, waste rope and other strong fibers. Binders' board comes in sheets made in a considerable range of thicknesses so that each book may have covers of a thickness appropriate to its size and weight.

If the book is to be covered with cloth (some variety of so-called buckram cloth is commonly used on library books) then this cloth is cut to fit the book; likewise a strip of paper is cut to fit the back of the book, this to be used as the "inlay" within the back of the cover. When boards, inlay, book and cloth are ready, the cloth is passed through the glueing machine which coats its one side with hot glue and delivers it on to a canvas belt or on to the work bench, glue side up.

There the operator, taking book and boards in his hands and locating the two boards so as to have just the proper "square," or projection over the edges of the trimmed volume, places the book side down on the freshly glued cloth suitably close to one end, places the inlay on the back between the boards, pulls the remainder of the cloth around the back and over the side of the book, turns in the edges, and the cover is made. Some binders first tip the boards lightly to the book with a little paste so that they will remain firmly in place during the covering operation.

The cover is immediately rubbed down with a bone folder, so that it may be given just the proper shape before the glue hardens. The covers are now thrown back and a heavy flour paste is applied to the end sheets, particularly to that portion of the back lining which extends over on to the end sheets, after which the covers are closed and the book goes into the press.

Books and press boards are laid alternately to form a stack that fills the press. The boards have raised metal edges which fit into the "French joints" of the books and when the pile has been made true and even, the powerful screw is turned tightly down and the books are kept in the press for twenty-four or more hours. When removed from the press they are piled under weights until quite dry. This insures a good shape and prevents the covers from curling, and may require several days' time, depending on weather conditions.

The books are now ready for what binders call "finishing," which in the library bindery means little more than "lettering" the title, author, and other requisite wording on the backs. This lettering is done with gold leaf and the permanency of the operation depends upon the suitable preparation of the cloth by means of a wash known as a "size"; the holding of the elusive gold leaf in position by means of a coat of oil on the cloth; the proper degree of heat in the brass type used (which heat must vary with atmospheric conditions), and finally the degree of manual skill that will insure not only the proper amount of pressure, but also accurate centering and alignment—for the lettering must be done one line at a time and its final appearance is entirely dependent upon the skill of the finisher.

The nature of the sizing used varies with the character of the fabric upon which it is applied, but the majority of formulas include principally egg albumen. White vaseline commonly serves as the oil for holding the gold leaf in position preparatory to lettering. After the lettering is done, all traces of the oil, along with adhering fragments of gold leaf, are removed by the use of naphtha, and the back of the book is given a thin coat of protective book lacquer.

The books are then finally inspected and entries made for billing purposes; then they are packed and shipped.

It is interesting to note that whether the order be large or small, about three to four weeks is required for the books to move step by step through the various processes incident to library binding.

The binding of periodicals into volumes for reference purposes forms a large part of the library binder's work. The actual operations are not greatly different from those already described, except that the preparation of the material is considerably more involved. Likewise the greater size of the volumes calls for added care in handling.

The first question preliminary to magazine binding is, what shall constitute a "volume," and does the volume have a title page and index? The answer is usually with the publisher, but the library binder is expected to know these facts so far as they pertain to the familiar periodicals that he is offered for binding.

For example, the "National Geographic Magazine" forms a volume each six months, beginning respectively in January and July, and it has a separate index and title page which are usually issued within sixty days after the completion of each volume. This index must be asked for, if it is desired. As another example, "House Beautiful" now forms its volumes half yearly also, although formerly it ran December to May and June to November, and the index was issued with the December number. Now the index comes separately. School periodicals, as for instance "Education," issue only ten numbers a year and form one volume, September to June. The index comes generally in the final issue of the volume. And so on through the list of hundreds of titles of periodicals which are sent to the binder; each publication is a law unto itself in the matter of its volume and index, and often a very uncertain law, as changes are of frequent occurrence. The library binder must keep a complete record covering data of this character, and the girls who prepare the volumes for binding must have convenient access to this file.

Another question pertaining to the formation of magazine volumes is whether the covers and advertisement pages, or either of them, are to be bound in. This should be covered on the librarian's order slip attached to the volume; nevertheless, in the absence of such instruction, the library binder must know the custom usually followed in this respect with regard to all ordinary periodicals.

When the wire stitches or the sewing threads have been removed and the necessary material is put together to make the volume complete, it is examined for page repairs, and then collated.

In cases where the paper is found to be spongy or wrinkled, the volume must be thoroughly pressed. Dampening the paper is a great help in this undertaking; therefore sponging the pages is resorted to when its nature will permit wetting.

Bound magazines are usually parts of sets and must therefore be made standard in height, covering, and lettering, for which purpose patterns or a "rub" with suitable notations are commonly made by the binder and filed for future reference. A rub of the lettering is produced in much the same way that children in their play make impressions of coins on paper, which they do by placing the paper firmly on the coin and then rubbing over it with a soft pencil, or crayon.

Newspapers and extra heavy volumes of magazines receive special care in the matter of attaching the covers to the body of the book. Some structural attachment in addition to an extra strong back lining is very desirable. This may take the form of cords or tapes across the backs of the volumes incorporated in the sewing, or it may be a flap of strong cloth sewed onto the edges of the book. If cords are used they are "laced" or inserted into holes in the board of the covers. In this manner the boards actually become an integral part of the book, and considerable added strength is obtained.

The term "reconstructed binding" is used to designate a division of library binding wherein bindings of new books are strengthened before they are put into use in the library, the idea being that there is added economy and convenience in rebinding the book at the very beginning in such a way that the cover will last as long as the paper. This is in contrast with the usual practice of circulating a book as originally bound by the publisher until it needs repairing and then rebinding it.

A reconstructed binding may be a rebinding, or it may actually be the very first binding, depending on whether it is possible to obtain the desired book from the publisher in unbound or sheet form. If already bound, the book must of course be removed from its cover and taken apart, and thereafter proceed essentially as already described earlier in this chapter.

In these cases, the original covers may be retained if their artistic or distinctive appearance is a controlling factor; otherwise a strong, lasting cover of library buckram or of a sound, acid-free leather replaces the publisher's more decorative but less-enduring cover.

A first binding generally starts with the complete books delivered by the publisher in the form of folded sheets. So the steps the books follow are first inspection, then sewing, backing and so on as already described.

In concluding it may be pointed out that, since library binding is primarily the business, or trade, of book *rebinding*, it may seem that the development of reconstructed bindings to any great extent must tend to displace rebinding and therefore destroy the present recognized business of library binding. However, this is scarcely apt to be the case, for it could be brought about only in the event that binderies which reconstruct new books become able to supply *any book at any place* in the country *at any time* when required by library purchasers. The impossibility of even approximating this under the present methods of publishing and distributing books gives assurance that the library binder will continue to have abundant work even in the face of the apparent competition of the reconstructed bindings.

The library binder is well aware that there is a

constantly increasing demand for more permanent books for public and school libraries. This would seem to assure an enduring place for the library binder in the branch of bookbinding which he has established and helped to standardize, and which has within the past decade become a recognized division of a great industry.

COPYRIGHTING

By Frederick H. Hitchcock

WHILE new books are being written by new authors and published by new publishers, there will always be an interest in and inquiry about the methods of protecting their rights in these literary productions.

In the first place, an author should remember that prior to publication he is, under the common law, the sole owner of his own literary work. Also, that it cannot be copyrighted in manuscript form. His first step, therefore, is to secure publication in either magazine or book form. This latter may be done by the author, himself, but is usually accomplished by an arrangement with a publisher. After talking over the terms of publication and coming to a verbal agreement with the publisher, the author will be asked to sign a contract.

Here is the author's first step in separating himself from a part of his ownership rights in his manuscript, for it is a common practice to have in the contract between the author and his publisher a clause assigning to the publisher all of the author's book rights for the "full term of copyright and for any and all renewals." The agreement, of course, will include other provisions, such as for the payment of the usual royalties, accounting, etc. Having been made before publication, such an assignment does not need to be recorded in the Copyright Office.

The book is then printed. The law requires that the copyright notice must be printed either on "the title-page or the page following," with the word "Copyright," or "copr.," accompanied by the name of the copyright proprietor, and the year of publication. Thus a copyright notice generally used in books will be found on the back of the title page reading like this "Copyright, 1929, by A. B." When the book has been published, this is a formal notification to the world that it is a copyrighted work and that no one else may make use of it without formal permission.

With this accomplished, the law requires that two complete copies of the best edition of the printed book be sent to the Register of Copyrights, in the Library of Congress at Washington, D. C. At the same time a fee of two dollars must be sent, together with a formal application for the registration of the copyright.

This application has to be made upon a blank number A1 supplied without charge by the Register of Copyrights. When filled out, it must be "solemnly affirmed," or sworn to, before a notary public. The information required includes the name and address of the copyright proprietor, the name of the author and the country of which he is a citizen, the title of the book, the date of publication, and the names and locations of the printer and of the binder, both of whom must be in the United States, for a book cannot be copyrighted unless it "has been printed from type set within the limits of the United States, or from plates made within the limits of the United States from type set therein," and unless "the binding of the said book was performed within the limits of the United States."

Perhaps the simplest method of sending the two copies to Washington is to deliver them to the nearest post-office where they will be accepted, receipted for and forwarded without charge to you. If this is done, the package should be left partly open so that the contents may be inspected by the postmaster. If this is not convenient, they can go by express with your name clearly written inside the package. In either case the sworn application and a postal money order for the amount of the fee ($2.00) must be sent in a separate stamped envelope. Checks, unless certified, are not accepted.

A short time after the two copies and the application for registration have reached the office of the Register of Copyrights, the certificate of registration will be returned in the mail. In its present form this is a card about 5 x 3 inches in size, on one side of which is printed:

"This is to certify, in conformity with section 55 of the Act to Amend and Consolidate the Acts respecting Copyright approved March 4, 1909, as amended by the Act approved March 2, 1913, that TWO copies of the Book named herein have been deposited in this Office under the provisions of the Act of 1909, together with the affidavit prescribed in section 16 thereof; and that registration of a claim to copyright for the first term of 28 years from the date of publication of said book has been duly made in the name of ———."

And on the reverse side will be written the name and address of the copyright owner, the title of the book, the name of the author and the name of the country of which the author is a citizen, the date of publication, the date on which the sworn application was received and the date when the two copies were received, and, also, the number and class of the entry.

The term of copyright runs for twenty-eight years from the date of first publication and may be renewed for a further term of twenty-eight years. Renewal can only be made by the author or his heirs and not by the publisher who may have become owner of the copyright. Copyrighting protects "all the copyrightable component parts of the work copyrighted" so that not only is the literary work of the author covered but also the illustrations, maps, or any other similar things that may make up the volume are protected. It ought to be remembered, however, that the title of a book is included only in connection with the text matter of the book, and that copyrighting a book does not necessarily give one the exclusive right to use a given title. Two or more books of entirely different nature are sometimes published with exactly the same titles by widely separated publishers, each of whom is quite ignorant of the other's action. All reputable publishers, however, make every effort to avoid using the title of another book, especially if there is the slightest reason to suspect that a real injury to another concern may result. A title can be trade-marked, however, and this was done for "Pollyanna."

There is one other everyday copyright matter that can well be mentioned here, namely the protecting of a book which has been published abroad in the English language and is to be published later in the United States. This may be accomplished by depositing in the copyright office, not later than sixty days after its publication abroad, one complete copy of the foreign edition, with a request for the reservation of the copyright and a statement of the name and nationality of the author and of the copyright proprietor and the day of foreign publication. This will secure an *ad interim* copyright which lasts for four months after the books have been deposited; within that period the book must be printed and bound in the United States and the details of copyrighting complied with as just explained.

Only the author or his assignee (i.e., the proprietor) may secure copyright in a book. An author may transfer orally all or part of his rights before publication, but after publication it is necessary for him to make the assignment by some form of written instrument. In order to make it a valid assignment, the original instrument must be sent to be recorded in the office of the Librarian of Congress within three months after its execution. The fee for recording an assignment is one dollar. After the original document has been recorded, it is recorded, signed and sealed and returned to the sender, who should preserve it with the certificate.

It is the custom with many publishers to establish the publication day of all of their books, by displaying a few copies, or by actually selling one or more copies to some one. In the case of a very popular copyrighted book which it is desirable to have the retailers all over the country begin to sell on the same day, it is deemed safer to make this technical publication before any of the books are distributed through the trade. A record of the first sales entered in a publisher's sales-book in the course of business would effectually prevent any one from claiming in after years a right to reprint a book on the ground that the claim, title, and copies were not originally filed until after the book had been put upon the market.

Under a recent amendment in our law, an author of a book in a foreign language, who is a citizen of one of the foreign countries which allows to our citizens the same copyright privileges as are allowed to its own countrymen, is permitted to file in the Copyright Office within thirty days after its publication in a foreign country a copy of his book with a formal declaration that he is the author and that he intends to translate it or to print it in its original language and to apply for copyright in the United States. After doing this, he is allowed one year in which to complete his proposed translation or to print it in the original language and copyright it here.

The history of copyright is an extremely interesting subject.

The first copyright law was enacted by Parliament during Queen Anne's reign, and is known as "8 Anne, c. 9." This statute provided that an author should have complete control of his literary productions during a first term of fourteen years after publication, and a renewal term of the same length, and provided penalties against piracy. Many questions concerning this law arose from time to time in trials before various courts, but perhaps the one of chief interest was that of whether the limitation of the period during which it granted protection, destroyed the author's rights which had existed previously. For fifty years after the passage of the law, the decisions were that the right of ownership existed for all time as a right in common law unaffected by the statute, but in 1774 the highest English court held that while the rights of the author before the publication of his book remained unaffected, after publication he had no rights except during the period specified by the statute. This decision is still believed by many authorities to have been a wrong one, but it has been the basis for all subsequent copyright law in this country as well as in England. Therefore in the United States today, the right of ownership lies in the author until his work is published, but upon publication he has no rights except those given him by law, and these he can obtain only by a strict compliance with the requirements of the law.   Any one who is sufficiently interested to read the first hundred pages of Drone's "Treatise on the Law of Property in Intellectual Productions" will be well repaid for the effort, and will obtain considerable light upon how the "right of copying," or printing, a book developed, why its duration is not unlimited, and why we must observe certain formalities in order to protect our literary work by it.

ADVERTISING AND PUBLICITY

By Joseph C. Pfeiffer

WHAT makes a book sell? This is a question which has vexed publishers, no doubt, for as many years as books have been published and seems no nearer a solution than it was in the days of the Phœnicians or Caxton, or whoever it was that first offered books for sale. Indeed, the publisher who first reduces the formula to a scientific basis so that he will select only books that the public wants and then launch them at precisely the right moment and in the right manner to secure the greatest possible distribution, is in line for a fortune that will surpass by many millions any that has been accumulated in the publishing business up to the present. Of course, not all books have been published for profit. There are philanthropic and endowed organizations which issue many books for the purpose of spreading information, and nearly every publisher brings out each season a few books which he knows will not return their investment but are of such high quality that he takes pride in having them bear his imprint.

But most publishing houses are business organizations conducted primarily for making money for their owners and it is of importance that the books issued each season have widespread and profitable distribution. Many people are involved in this distribution but the work of bringing these publications to the attention of the public so that they will go to the stores and buy requires a properly organized promotion department.

Book promotion, as it is conducted today, divides itself into two operations, or, we might say, departments: Advertising, for which the publisher pays, and Publicity, which he gets for little or nothing. Few other manufacturers of merchandise sold through retail stores have the opportunity to secure free publicity that is open to the book publisher. It is not possible for the maker of canned goods, shoes or gadgets to get his wares commented upon almost daily in the press without paying for it. But books, being in the nature of news, are reviewed by hundreds of newspapers, weekly journals and monthly magazines, and their authors, being regarded, in a sense, as celebrities, are subjects for various types of interviews and human interest stories, so that many channels of free publicity are open to the publisher to supplement his regular paid advertising and promotion.

In some of the larger publishing houses advertising and publicity are made separate departments, the advertising being an integral part of the sales organization, while the distribution of publicity is handled in the editorial division and its purely commercial aspects kept as much in the background as possible. However, the efforts of the two must frequently coincide and overlap and most houses, therefore, find it desirable to have one person direct both advertising and publicity and be responsible for the general promotion of the books published. The duties of this department are so complicated and manifold that it is not possible to discuss them all at length within the space of a single chapter. But an attempt will be made here to set down briefly the major activities involved in book advertising and publicity, for the type of publisher that sells his product largely through retail stores, and the description will be confined in the main to a statement of the actual practice rather than of the underlying philosophy.

ADVERTISING

The work of the advertising department of a book publisher begins as soon as a manuscript is accepted and the season of its publication determined upon. The first step is the preparation of the basic material upon which most of the subsequent advertising and publicity program is to hinge. The advertising manager must acquaint himself fully with the contents of each book. He must know just what the author was seeking to accomplish when he wrote the book, what audience it was intended for, how wide its appeal is to be, what the editor's ideas are regarding it, and what the hopes and expectations of the firm are as to its marketability.

It is well to prepare typewritten sheets on which all

of these facts are set down in brief, together with a synopsis of the book, a table of contents, biography of the author and a list of sales helps. These sheets are generally compiled jointly by the editorial and advertising departments and copies of them are not only kept on file in each department but are also furnished to the sales manager for his salesmen.

For convenience in selling, most publishing houses divide the year into two seasons and arrange their new publications in two groups which they call their spring and fall lists. The spring list generally comprises the books to be published between January and July; the fall list those coming between July and December. As soon as the titles for a season are determined upon, the advertising department sets about to prepare a descriptive catalog or list. These lists are first printed for the use of salesmen, for the preliminary guidance of booksellers and for general office use, and are of necessity subject to change and revision. Only a small quantity, therefore, is printed at first. Sometimes two or three editions are printed in a season, with changes and revisions, and when the list becomes as nearly complete as it is possible to have it and the facts about all books are known, a large quantity of this descriptive catalog is often printed for distribution to libraries, booksellers, literary editors, and sometimes to the general public. Much care and thought is given to the physical appearance of these lists. They are frequently illustrated with reproductions of jackets, pictures from books, and photographs of

authors, and in typography and printing reflect the taste
of the publisher and give some indication of the care
with which his books are selected and manufactured. At
the same time that the descriptive list of new books is
prepared, the complete catalog in which the publications
of previous years are listed, is revised and brought up
to date. Small publishers frequently combine the new
list and the catalog of older publications. The larger
houses, whose books run into thousands of titles, keep the
type standing at the printer's for their general catalogs
and the advertising department makes corrections and
orders new printings as often as is necessary.

The next duty of the advertising department is the
preparation of jacket material. The paper wrappers in
which books are enclosed are nothing more than silent
salesmen who, by their originality and general attractive-
ness, whet the appetite of the prospective purchaser and
encourage him to buy. The original paper jacket was
simply a strip of plain white or manila paper with a round
hole punched in it so that the title on the shelf back of
the book would show through. It was intended for protective purposes only. Later, for convenience in handling, publishers began to print titles and brief descriptions on the front of the jacket. From this simple
beginning the modern, highly decorative and appealing
jacket has developed; but it is there primarily for the
purpose of advertising the book. The entire jacket,
therefore, ought to be devised by the advertising department in consultation with editors and those responsible

for manufacture. Some publishers prefer to have the front of the jacket and the paper upon which it is printed determined by the editors, the art editor or the manufacturing manager, and the advertising department simply supplies the "blurbs" or descriptive material that goes on the front, the inside flaps and the back.

It is generally recognized that the enthusiastic support of booksellers is needed if a book intended for wide distribution is to secure its maximum sale. Consequently the advertising department is responsible for securing the interest and support of the bookseller for each book to be published.

At the outset, then, the advertising department plans a campaign of sales letters, circulars and advertising in the trade papers to supplement the work of the sales force in securing the initial order of the bookseller. It also must plan the material which is to aid the bookseller to display the books and get rid of them after they reach his shop.

Sometimes sales letters to retail booksellers are prepared by the sales manager. More often, however, the advertising department works these out. Since books are now published every month in the year and frequently come out before the salesmen can call upon all of the book trade, the publisher has to depend upon these letters and the circular material accompanying them to secure the initial order of many retailers. A great deal of thought is consequently expended upon this promotion material and much ingenuity is shown in devising ways to catch the eye of the dealer who is constantly deluged with advertising material.   Public libraries, which are one of the largest outlets for the consumption of books, are handled in much the same manner as the bookseller, and receive the same promotion material. The trade paper schedule of advertising is generally planned well in advance and is of two kinds: preliminary announcements of new books, and advertisements run after books have been published to inform the retailer of the success which they are achieving.

The advertising department next turns its attention to dealer helps.   One of the most effective means of getting books before the public is through special display in booksellers' windows. If a book is likely to have a considerable popular sale so that the expense is warranted, posters, show cards and other display material are prepared.   The number and variety of display posters is endless.   Generally such material is made in quantity for widespread distribution.   Occasionally elaborate mechanical, electrical, or other special window display outfits are prepared and shipped from one store to another throughout the season.   Post cards or small circulars of all kinds, of a size to fit into a commercial envelope, are frequently made up and furnished to booksellers to be sent out at the time a new book is published. The arrangement for the distribution of this material is generally made by the salesmen when soliciting orders from booksellers.   There are also numerous catalogs, house organs and monthly lists compiled for distribution by booksellers and in these publishers run advertising or make special arrangements to have their books featured.

After the campaign to and for the bookseller is worked out and the book is still in process of manufacture, the advertising department comes to the most important and most difficult phase of its work—the problem of display advertising to appear in newspapers and magazines. Some houses attempt to estimate roughly the probable total business of the season and from that figure set aside a sum for display advertising purposes. Most publishers, however, prefer the less hazardous plan of fixing a definite amount for each book, based upon the number of copies to be printed in the first edition. This figure is arrived at, in some houses, by estimating ten per cent of the total wholesale receipts from the first edition. That is, if $1.20 is the average wholesale price at which the book is sold to the bookseller and the first printing is 2000 copies, a sum of $240.00 is appropriated for the initial advertising campaign.

This represents the most conservative method. Not a few publishers figure ten per cent of the *retail* price rather than the wholesale price for their more popular books. There are also other considerations frequently involved, such as promises to the author; and each season nearly every publisher has a few books upon which he is willing to gamble a sum considerably greater than either of the above percentages because he believes that the chances of success for these books are very great if they can be properly started. (The foregoing percentages apply only to books such as are generally distributed through booksellers. Subscription sets and other books which are sold direct to the public require much larger advertising appropriations.) Each book then is considered and a sum appropriated for its promotion. To this are added varying sums for continuing the live books of the previous season and for general house promotion.

When the preliminary budget is arrived at, the advertising department must decide upon the manner and amount of advertising to be done. At this point many publishers employ the services of a well equipped agency specializing in book advertising. The agency, with its professional knowledge of what newspapers and magazines reach the largest audience of book buyers at a cost not prohibitive, draws up a preliminary schedule which is submitted to the publisher. This is discussed and rearranged to suit special conditions, and when approved the agency then prepares the initial advertising copy. If no agency is employed, all this must be done in the advertising department of the publishing house. For books likely to have a popular sale individual advertisements are prepared, the size and number of insertions depending upon the amount available as shown in the budget. If a book catches public favor and has a lively sale the separate advertisements are continued; if not, the title is included in group advertisements for the balance of the season. Books of minor importance and volumes that may enjoy a long life but never a large sale in any one season are advertised in groups. Special or class books such as business, scientific, technical and similar publications are advertised chiefly in class papers reaching an audience especially interested.

As to nature of copy to be used in advertisements and what is considered good and bad advertising, no two people will ever agree and it is useless to attempt to set down a formula. Originality, knowledge of public taste at the moment, quick recognition of shifting tastes, and clear and convincing means of expression are contributing factors. There are many experienced advertising men who know when advertising is good and when it is bad but their knowledge is founded upon long training and experience and is scarcely transferable.

The book publisher has not the opportunity that other manufacturers have to test out his advertising. The life of the average book, fiction at least, is short and the sum available for advertising is infinitesimally small, compared to the great budgets spent by automobile, radio and household commodity manufacturers. He can seldom afford a nation-wide campaign and can do little experimenting. A big manufacturer, using pages in many magazines, found that the simple changing of a headline from Cold Feet to Warm Feet increased his business tremendously. But the book publisher seldom advertises on a scale sufficiently large to notice such influences. It is nevertheless easy to waste considerable sums of money in display advertising campaigns and publishers have found, just as other advertisers, that no expenditures will force a public to buy something in which it is not interested. On the other hand, many a book has failed of large sale because the publisher stopped his promotion just at the turn of success. And some astute publishers have reaped large rewards because they were quick to sense the upward trend toward popularity and kept up their advertising program until the book was firmly established in the minds of the buying public.

In order to have successful advertising there must be the closest possible co-operation between the advertising and sales departments of the publishing house. Each must be thoroughly aware of the other's activities and be prepared to take every advantage of them. Salesmen should know what advertising is being done and should carry with them whenever possible samples of advertisements as a part of their selling equipment. The advertising manager should know from day to day just what success the sales force is having with each book: and whenever it is possible to determine it should know just how much the advertising is helping to develop sales.

It is the sale of a book after the first printing that determines whether advertising is to be continued. If a book is selling rapidly, additions to the original budget should be promptly made. Indeed, it is frequently desirable to abandon the first schedule and work out another, larger and more comprehensive, to accelerate sales while the book is moving and the interest of booksellers, reviewers and public is at its height. Some of the most successful publishers, during the first season of a book, go over the advertising schedule weekly and make changes based upon sales during the preceding week. This is especially desirable when reviews are enthusiastic and when the general public response is widespread and favorable. The original advertising budget laid out in conservative fashion by the publisher at the opening of the season is, therefore, frequently only a part of what he spends if the books live up to the expectations of editor and author.

The advertising methods heretofore described in this chapter apply chiefly to the more popular types of books such as fiction, biography and occasional best sellers in other fields. Nearly every publisher brings out each season a number of books, the initial sale of which is likely not to be large but which, because of their importance and usefulness, will continue to sell over a long period of years. These books cannot be promoted by the methods applied to fiction and the big sellers. Many of them are intended for special audiences. To reach these people promotion methods are employed involving the judicious distribution of well planned letters or circular material. This necessitates a section of the advertising department being delegated to handling material for circular promotion. The size and equipment of this division depends upon the number of general or special books which the publisher issues and the extent to which he wishes to develop this type of selling. The circular division starts work far in advance of publication of each book, gathers lists of prospects, prepares sales letters, makes tests of the "pulling power" of the advertising material and finally handles the distribution of this material in detail. The extent of the circularizing program depends at the outset upon the selling price of the book, the margin of profit available for promotion purposes and the ease with which prospects may be interested. Sometimes only a single letter or a single leaflet is sent out. Sometimes a series of letters or a number of different types of circulars are sent to each list. The methods of subscription book publishers are very elaborate and their circularizing organizations are often of enormous size and capacity. Nearly every publisher has to do a certain amount of circular distribution each season but not all publishers attempt to get direct business from this type of promotion. Some prefer to have the sales go to booksellers although they believe that the proper distribution of circular material on those books which seem to have a special appeal to lists of people primarily interested, will stimulate sales more quickly than display advertising in newspapers and magazines. These publishers, then, send out circulars to special lists from their own offices or arrange to have booksellers distribute them, but make no effort to secure sales direct. Some publishers send circular material only to booksellers and to public libraries, which are, of course, one of the chief outlets for the sale of books.

Other publishers have built up large and well classified lists of individual book buyers to whom they regularly send descriptive material, and a force of clerks is kept busy accumulating and checking lists, addressing, mailing and in the other activities of circularization.

Many minor activities fall to the advertising department of the book publisher but these vary greatly according to the size of the publishing house and its business methods, and will not be commented upon here. As every book in a publisher's list is an individual item requiring separate attention, the advertising manager's job is a complicated one enmeshed in detail, and his usefulness to his firm depends upon his ability to get the details handled smoothly and quickly so that no book will be neglected and the greatest possible time allowed in which to plan new ideas for promotion.

PUBLICITY

Many good books have been written about Advertising, but few about Publicity, for while modern study and investigation have succeeded in reducing advertising to a fairly scientific basis, publicity must ever remain an art, depending for its success more upon the imagination, the astuteness and the personality of the publicity director than upon the means and methods employed. To be sure, there must be certain definite machinery employed in every well run publicity department, but the results achieved by this machinery depend almost wholly upon the mind of the directing head.

The opportunities open to publicity for books are unlimited. Quite apart from the usual reviews or criticisms, there is a "human interest story," sometimes several, behind every book written. Even the dry-as-dust tome, the deadly volume of statistics, the formidable excursions into the realms of philosophy and theology, have hidden away in them somewhere little bits of interesting information, sprightly stories, facts pertinent to the news of the moment, or other material which some magazine or newspaper editor will be glad to have to fill his columns and the publication of which will draw attention to the book. And what author ever refused an interview under proper circumstances?

Publicity probably is responsible for the success of more books than paid advertising. It begins, very often, months before the book is published; sometimes, indeed, before the author has finished the manuscript. Little stories about a forthcoming publication, cleverly planned and properly circulated, sometimes grow in magnitude until a considerable part of the reading public is feverishly awaiting the publication date of a book. When the book actually appears, publicity supplements and increases the effect of the advertising campaign, and it keeps a book in the literary news columns long after the advertising budget has been exhausted.

The mechanics of publicity are not complicated. Every publishing house must have an up-to-date card index containing the names of papers which review books, their literary editors, the days of the week or month upon which the book pages appear, and a few facts about each paper's policy, whether it prints news items and gossip in addition to reviews, whether it uses illustrated material, photographs of authors, and so forth.

When a book is about to appear for the first time, the publicity director goes over these names and makes up a list of papers to receive copies for review. He must know, consequently, something of the taste of the literary editors and the audience which each paper reaches. There are actually hundreds of newspapers, weekly journals and magazines which review books. No publisher can possibly afford to send copies to all of these. The publicity director must keep the number of review copies sent out down to reasonable proportions or great wastage is apt to result. Sometimes, he accompanies the review copy with a letter pointing out certain facts which he thinks may interest the editor, for he knows that while most editors conduct their columns in independent fashion, it is not possible for an editor to know what all the leading books of the season are to be, and a brief description will help him to determine the value of each book and assign it to a competent reviewer.

To supplement the review copies, the publicity director sends out at regular intervals announcements of forthcoming publications, news and gossip about books and authors, in the form of short notes designed chiefly for publication in papers having literary columns. These gossip sheets are often set in type and printed; more frequently they are multigraphed or typewritten. Some publishers send out such material each week not only to literary editors but to numerous other lists of people interested in the circulation of books. The publicity director has lists of buyers for bookstores and of retail clerks, of librarians and the managers of circulating libraries, and he sees that all of these are kept well informed about his books.

The publicity director conducts an enormous correspondence with people of all kinds who are in a position to give publicity to books. He has lists of all types of newspaper people: editorial writers, Sunday editors, city editors, editors of women's pages and home magazine pages, interviewers, conductors of humorous columns. Sometimes he sends the book itself, sometimes a note, sometimes a special story, often nothing more than just a line or two which may result in publicity. He knows the leading lecturers and platform speakers who are in a position to recommend books to vast audiences. He is in touch with the people of the radio, dramatic and motion picture world, with clergymen and pulpit orators, with people prominent in public life whose opinions will have influence on sales. Not only does he endeavor to secure the co-operation of these people in commenting upon or mentioning his books but he collects favorable opinions from every available source, which the advertising and sales department can use to advantage in their promotion work.

Many books get free publicity through their own news interest or their close tie-up to the news of the day. The alert publicity manager watches the news columns of the press at all times and takes full advantage of every opportunity for a tie-up. If "companionate marriage" is the subject of the moment he gets the authors of his new books interviewed on companionate marriage. He searches through all of his publications, old and new, for chapters and extracts which have anything bearing on the subject. He writes or has written special articles on the subject, in some part of which reference is made to one or more of these books. Many of the articles and stories appearing in the special magazine sections of newspapers have their origin in the publicity department of publishing houses.

Sometimes the publication of a book is of such interest that a front page news story in leading papers may be readily obtained. The publicity director sees that all of the newspapers in his immediate vicinity have the book the same day so that the news stories appear simultaneously. He also arranges with the telegraphic press bureaus such as the Associated Press and the United Press to have news stories sent out to all of their affiliated papers.

The publicity manager keeps a file of illustrated material, photographs of authors, etc. Sometimes a large number of copies of an author's photograph are made and sent out with review copies of books. Frequently, photographs are distributed with special interviews or short notes about the author. Illustrations from books are often made into newspaper matrixes and sent out to editors. The publicity director knows the editors of rotogravure sections and supplies them with copies of interesting pictures from books, such as travel books, as well as pictures of authors and scenes of their home life. A group of interesting photographs is often the basis of a good magazine article or Sunday feature story about an author and his work.

No one can outline a definite program for a publicity manager and he himself does not know at the opening of the season just what opportunities will arise for publicity for books. His work develops from day to day and its effectiveness depends upon his energy, ingenuity and awareness of all that is going on about him. He is un-questionably one of the most important factors in present-day book distribution.

THE TRAVELING SALESMAN

By Harry A. Thompson

With Revision by Samuel McLean Loweree

THE increase in the visible supply of authors more than meets the demand. A manuscript once accepted, the publisher finds no lack of paper makers ready to supply him with any grade of fair white paper that he may wish to spoil. Printers even manifest a dignified alacrity to set the type and print the book, and binders are yet to be accused of any disinclination to cover it.

It is only when author, paper maker, printer, and binder have done with their share in the exploitation of literature that the publisher finds that the current which has been urging him gently onward has set against him. Of making many books there is no end, but the profitable marketing of the same is vanity and vexation of spirit.

Enter the salesman.

He is to convince the bookseller, who is to convince the public, that this particular book—shall we, for our purpose, christen it "Last Year's Nests"?—is the great American novel, and that its influence on the reading of unborn generations will be measured by the rank it holds in the list of the six best sellers.

The salesman is handicapped not a little by the fact that it is neither shoes, nor pig-iron, nor even mess-pork that he is selling, and, therefore, superior quality of workmanship, inferior price, and personal magnetism count for little. Persuasiveness, which, perhaps, is a part of personal magnetism, counts; so does an intelligent knowledge of the contents of the look; likewise hard work and tactful persistence; also, honesty. But opposed against the combination is the bookseller, on guard against overstocking, to some extent a purchaser of a pig in a poke, conscious that one unsold book eats up the profit on five copies safely disposed of.

Time was when good salesmanship consisted in overstocking a bookseller; this was occasioned less by persuasiveness than by overpersuasiveness. Regardless of the merits of the book and with no more than a nodding acquaintance with its contents, a persuasive salesman could "load" a customer—as he called it out of the customer's hearing—with two hundred and fifty or five hundred copies of a novel that had no other merit than that it had been written by a novelist whose previous book had met with success. The significance of these figures, two hundred and fifty and five hundred is to be found in the additional discount to retailers on these quantities. Latterly, the publisher has found that a bankrupt bookseller has few creditors besides publishers, and has come to a realizing sense of the futility of clogging the distributing machinery. He is disposed, therefore, to exercise some restraint upon his salesman's ardor. Perhaps it were better to say that the salesman is more disposed to aid the bookseller in his purchases to the end that no monuments of unsold failures will stare him in the face on his next visit to the customer's store.

All of which, while interesting to the historian of the publishing trade, carries us too far in advance of our text. Let us therefore return to "Last Year's Nests"— 12mo, cloth, illustrated, stained top, price $2.00.

The first edition—it may be one thousand copies or ten thousand—has been delivered to the publisher by the binder, who alone, in some instances, knows his profit on them. "Last Year's Nests" is by a well-known author, and contains some elements of popularity. The literary adviser has written an appreciation of it, one of the stenographers has declared it grand, and the salesman, if he is given to reading, says it's a corker. He starts out with it; along with a trunkful of other books, to be sure, but our sympathies are wholly with the "Nests," and it is only that career we shall follow.

He may be one of a force of salesmen, each of whom has his own territory. One may visit only the larger cities, Boston, New York, Philadelphia, Pittsburgh, Chicago; another may take in the smaller towns along this route; another, the Middle West, Southern or Southwestern territory. Still another, the cities west of Chicago, including those on the Pacific coast. Houses publishing competitive lines and non-copyright books

have other methods and machinery for distribution. I
speak only for the copyright salesman, and not to be
too prolix, take only the copyright novel as an illustration of the day's work.

The salesman arrives at a town, say Chicago. He
goes to the hotel, and orders his trunks to his room and
unpacks and arranges his books on a table as effectively
as his artistic sense permits. Then he visits his customers
and makes appointments that cover a full week. Previous
to his arrival his office had informed the booksellers of
his coming, enclosing a catalog. This the bookseller
handed to a clerk to be marked up. The clerk had gone
over their stock of this particular publisher's books and
had marked opposite each title in the catalog the number of copies on hand. Armed with this catalog the
bookseller keeps his appointment at the room of the
traveler. [It ought to be mentioned in passing that this
is a purely hypothetical case, invented for the purposes
of illustration. The clerk who marks up the catalog
in advance of the salesman's arrival is as fictitious as the
bookseller who keeps his appointment promptly. Perhaps this delightful uncertainty is another of the many
influences that make the book business, from the writing
of the manuscript to the reading of the printed book, so
fascinating.]

In the salesman's room the customer examines the
new books, asks questions, hears arguments (many of
them fearfully and wonderfully made), and eventually,
after much debate, gives his order. Having ordered all

the new books that he wishes, he goes over the catalog and gives what is called his stock order; that is to say, he orders the books on which his stock is low but for which there is still a demand.

Perhaps the salesman has reserved for his final battle the sale of "Last Year's Nests." As prices cut some figure in this argument, we are driven, for a moment, to the dry bones of prices and discounts.

Listed in the publisher's catalog at $2.00, the ordinary discount to a dealer ordering two or three copies is thirty-three and one-third per cent, or $1.34 net, the bookseller paying transportation charges. Competition, however, has increased this discount to forty per cent, so that we shall assume that in small quantities the book can be had at $1.20 net. In large quantities extra discounts are given; some publishers give an extra 1 cent on 500—2 cents on 1000 and so on; the quantity necessary in order to secure this extra price is usually determined by the popularity of the author. But, as has been pointed out, the growing tendency is not to overload the bookseller, especially in view of the fact that it is the publisher who loses when the bookseller assigns.

Assuming that "Last Year's Nests" is likely to have a large sale and that the salesman wishes to sell Mr. Bookseller two hundred and fifty copies, he would probably quote an extra discount on that quantity. If he can persuade the bookseller to take two hundred and fifty copies, he has not only swollen his sales by that amount, but he has forced a probable retail sale of that quantity. For once on the bookseller's tables, the very size of the order inspires every clerk to help reduce the pile, not to mention the fact that the books are bought and must be paid for. Had the bookseller bought five copies, extra efforts towards sales would not be forthcoming; the energy would be applied to another novel. Hence the salesman's efforts to effect a large sale.

There is another reason for this extra quantity. Two hundred and fifty copies of "Last Year's Nests," piled in a pyramid, is a gentle reminder to the bookseller's customers that it is an important book. Such an argument is often more potent than the disagreeing opinions of critics. Here is a case in point.

A novelist wrote an altogether charming and spirited novel. The reviewers spoke well of it, but the sale of the book hung fire. It was the dull season and there was no other novel of any worth in the public mind. The salesman said to his employer: "Here's a book that has a good chance for success. If you'll back me with some good advertising, I'll guarantee to make that novel sell."

The publisher replied: "Go ahead, my son; I'll take a gamble on it." (They really talk that way when they travel mufti.) So the salesman induced the New York wholesalers to take a large quantity guaranteeing to take back the books if they were not sold.

Next the retail booksellers were asked to take a number of copies on the same terms, and pile them conspicuously in their stores.

Then an advertising campaign was planned. Critics

there were a-plenty who wagged a sad head because the advertising was undignified. What they meant was that it was unconventional, was without the dignity of tradition to give it its hall-mark. It had, at least, the novelty of originality, and answered the final test of good advertising in that it attracted attention. Then the sale began, and as soon as New York City was reporting it among the list of the six best sellers, the salesman took to the road to carry on the campaign. The result was eventually a sale reaching six figures.

But to get back to "Last Year's Nests." It is to be published June 1. A few sample pages only have been printed, but blank paper fills out to the bulk of the book as it will be. Illustrations—if they are ready—are inserted, the title-page printed, and the whole is bound up in a sample cover. This is technically known as a dummy, and serves to show the prospective buyer merely the outward and visible sign of an inward and spiritual appeal to public favor. For the purpose of informing the bookseller it is worth but little more than the printed title or a catalog announcement. Yet the bookseller likes to handle something tangible when he is making up his order, and the salesman, with even a dummy in his hand, finds that there is less wear and tear upon his imagination.

Were he selling shoes, the salesman would, as a matter of course, point out the superior quality of the goods, lay stress on their style and durability, and as a clincher, present the incontrovertible argument of low price. On no such brief can the book salesman rest his case. "Last Year's Nests" varies in no respect mechanically from any of its 12mo competitors; and if it did, it would make no difference.

Two arguments and two only comprise the salesman's stock in trade; if he can say that "Last Year's Nests" is by the well-known author whose name is a household word and whose previous book sold so many thousand copies, he has the bookseller on the mourner's bench; if he can (and he frequently does) add the clinching argument that his firm will advertise the book heavily, he can leave the bookseller with that thrill of triumph we all feel when we bend another's will to our own.

A young and inexperienced salesman, whom we shall call Mr. Green, was making his Western trip. As he was waiting in a bookseller's store for his customer's attention, there entered a traveler of ripe years and experience, representing one of the larger publishing firms. Naturally the bookseller gave the older salesman his instant attention. With no desire to eavesdrop, Mr. Green could not avoid overhearing the conversation.

"Hello, Blank! Anything new?"

"Yes, I have a big novel here by a big man. It will have a big sale," and Blank mentioned the title and author.

At this point, Green pricked up his ears. He had read the novel in manuscript form and his immediate thought was, "Here's where I learn something about the gentle art of making sales."

Mr. Blank proceeded to tell what he knew about the book. His synopsis was so inaccurate that Green knew that he had not read the book, but was glibly misquoting the publisher's announcement. Green's courage was fired as he reflected how much better he could have portrayed the chief incidents of the plot. But his triumph was momentary. Blank ended his argument in a voice that left no doubt of his own faith in the effectiveness of his logic. "And the firm is going to advertise it like ——."

"Send me two hundred and fifty copies," said the customer.

The longer Mr. Green traveled the more convinced he became that the old salesman knew his business. The argument of advertising carries with it a certain persuasiveness that the customer cannot resist. Not always does a liberal use of printer's ink land a book among the six best sellers; but it does it so often that the rule is proved by the exception. A publisher once made the statement, in the presence of a number of men interested in the book-publishing business, that, by advertising, he could sell twenty thousand copies of any book, no matter how bad it was. The silence of the others indicated assent to the doctrine. But one inquiring mind broke in with the question, "But can you make a profit on it?"

"Ah! That is another question," answered the publisher.

And the ledgers of several publishers will show a loss, due to excessive advertising, on books that loom large in public favor. The author has reaped good royalties and the salesman has had no great draft made upon his stock of persuasive argument.

It is under such circumstances that the traveler finds his work easy and his burden light. Another condition under which he meets with less resistance is in the instance of a second book by an author whose first book has met with success. The bookseller is a wary, cautious man; what illusions he once had have gone down the corridors of time along with the many books that have not helped him. For reasons that are not so inscrutable as they may seem to the enthusiastic salesman, the bookseller is disinclined to order more than a few copies of a first book by a new author. Perhaps the traveler has read the book and is surcharged with enthusiasm; he talks eloquently and ably in the book's behalf; he masses argument upon argument—and in the end makes about as much impression as he would by shooting putty balls at the Sphinx. Even though the salesman's enthusiasm may find its justification in the reviewer's opinions and the beginning of a brisk sale for the book all over the country, still the reluctant bookseller broods moodily over the past and refuses to be stung again. But let the book have a large sale and then let the salesman start out with a second book by this author, the bookseller, with few exceptions, will go the limit on quantity. Unfortunately, it frequently happens that the public—which is a discriminating public or not, as you chance to look at it—does not seem possessed of the same blind confidence, and the result may be a monument of unsold copies.

The trade, I think, is coming more and more to be guided by the advice of such salesmen as have proved to be the possessors of judgment and honesty. By judgment is meant not merely the opinion that one forms of the literary value of a book, but that commercial estimate that a good salesman is able to make. The literary adviser can state in terms of literary criticism the reasons why the manuscript is worthy of publication; but the traveler, if he happens to be more than a mere peddler, can, after reading it, take pencil and paper and figure out about how many copies he can place. Publishers are growing to appreciate this quality in a salesman and are seeking his advice before accepting a manuscript. Some go further and ask his assistance in the make-up of a book; for a good cover covers a multitude of sins.

In former years it was considered the salesman's first duty to "load" the customer; that is, sell him all he could, regardless of the merits of the books. In those days a denial of the good old doctrine that the imprint could do no wrong was rank heresy. Such salesmen are no longer categoried with Cæsar's wife, and the new salesmanship is having its day. Its members are men of reading and intelligence, who have taken the trouble to learn something about the wares they are selling, and who have found that it pays to be honest. It doesn't seem to pay the first year; but if the salesman's judgment of books is discriminating and he hangs on, the booksellers soon realize that they can trust him. As they know little of the new books he is offering, they are inclined to be guided by his advice; should they find that this pays, they will repose more confidence in him. A traveler who, in lieu of personal imagination and the power of persuasion, was forced to depend upon hard work and the common, or garden, kind of honesty for what success he had on the road, was giving up his work to take an indoor position. On his final trip he had a "first" book by a "first" author; it was an unusual book and had in it possibilities of a really great sale. The firm publishing the book was in the hands of an assignee. The outlook was not propitious for a large sale: a new book by an unknown author published by an assignee. But the salesman believed in the book, believed in it with judgment and enthusiasm. "I found," he said, in telling the story, "that the trade to a man believed in me. It affected me deeply to feel that my years of straight dealing had not been wasted. The booksellers backed me up, bought all the copies I asked them to buy,—and I asked largely,—with the result that I sold ten thousand copies in advance of publication. The firm has sold since over two hundred thousand copies of that book and its creditors received a hundred cents on the dollar."

It would seem an axiom that a man selling books should have at least a bowing acquaintance with their contents, yet I have heard salesmen argue hotly in favor of the old-time salesman who sold books as he would sell shoes or hats. Such a one was selling a novel to a

Boston bookseller. He had not taken the trouble to read the book, but had been told by his firm that it was a good story. Flushed with the vehemence of his own argument for a large order, he floundered about among such vague statements as: "You can't go to sleep until you have finished it! It's great! A corking story! Can't lay the book down! Unable to turn out the light until you have read the last line!"

"But what's it about?" quickly interrupted the customer, suspecting that the traveler had not read the book.

"It's about—it's about two dollars," was the quick retort.

Perhaps here we find the substitute for the reading that maketh a full man. Repartee of this sort is disarming, and the quickness of wit that prompts it is not one of the least useful attributes of salesmanship. To carry the moral a step farther, it is only fair to say that the nimble salesman has had the wit to get out of the publishing business into another line of industry that, if reports are to be believed, has made him independent.

The commercial traveler who sells books has no fault to find with the people with whom he deals. By the very nature of his calling the bookseller is a man of reading and culture; now and then among them you find a man of rare culture. So genuinely friendly are the relations existing between seller and purchaser that a traveling man has the feeling that he is making a pleasure trip among friends. Such relations are no mean asset to the salesman, although they are not wholly essential. For it is to the bookseller's interest at least to examine the samples of every publisher's representative. It is not a question of laying in the winter's supply of coal, or of being content with one good old standby line of kitchen ranges. It is books that he is dealing in; an article that knows no competition and that has a brief career. Should my lady ask for Mark Twain's last book, it would be a poor bookseller who answered, "We don't sell it, but we have a large pile of Marie Corelli's latest." Or should the customer desire a copy of one of Henry James's volumes, what would it profit the bookseller to inform her that he did not have it in stock, but he had something just as good?

It is because of the immense numbers of titles the bookseller must carry that the salesman always finds him a willing listener. And in the end, even though he does not buy heavily, he must order at least a few each of the salable books. Such complacency on the part of the bookseller might argue for direct dealing on the part of the publisher by means of circulars and letters, thus saving the expense of a traveler. But firms that have tried this have had a change of heart and have quickly availed themselves of the traveler's services.

He is useful in ways other than selling. If he is keen to advance his firm's interests—and most of the book travelers are—he will interest the bookseller's clerks in the principal books of his line. He will send them a copy of an important book, knowing that the clerk, should he become interested in the book, will personally sell many copies.

In the matter of credits, the traveling man is of considerable service to his house. He is on the spot, can size up the bookseller's trade, note if he is overstocked, particularly with unsalable books, or "plugs," as they are called, obtain the gossip of the town, and in many ways can form an estimate of the bookseller's financial condition that is more trustworthy than any the credit man in the home office can get. There were a dozen publishers' representatives who once sat in solemn conclave discussing the financial responsibility of an important customer. He was suspected of being beyond his depth, and some of the travelers had been warned not to sell him. Several personally inspected his business, obtained a report from him and his bank, and threshed out the matter as solemnly and seriously as if they were the interested publishers whom they represented. It was decided to extend further credit to the bookseller; his orders were taken and sent in with full explanations. How many orders were rejected by the publishers I do not, of course, know. But the judgment of the travelers, as events proved, was justified.

The publisher is learning to regard his traveling man as more than a salesman. He is asking him, now and then, to assist him in the selection of a manuscript, to aid him in planning the letter-press, and binding of a book. For by the very nature of his work the traveler is the one man in the publisher's employ who has a comprehensive grasp of the many branches of this alluring business.

SELLING AT WHOLESALE

By Francis Ludlow

THE chief function of the book wholesaler is to maintain such a complete stock of the books in current demand as will enable him to fill promptly and economically all orders which he may receive from bookstores in any part of the country. He buys books in large quantities and sells them in small quantities. He is, therefore, a distributor, or jobber. But because he acts as an intermediary between publisher and retail bookseller, the wholesaler has become much more than a jobber, for besides buying from publishers and reselling to retailers, he performs countless other important subsidiary operations. So he must have a complex and departmentalized organization, a large part of which neither buys nor sells. His importance to the book trade is evident in the fact that about three-fourths of those who deal in books in this country are to a greater or less extent jobber's customers.

"To buy books in large quantities" seems a simple task, but it is, nevertheless, difficult and complicated.

In order to buy at all, the wholesaler must open negotiations with publishers both here and abroad, not only with the many well-known publishing houses but with hundreds of others who issue perhaps only one book. He must be on the lookout constantly for new publishers, and once he has entered into correspondence with any of them, must establish credit relations, fix upon discount schedules with them, and arrange to keep in close contact with them thereafter.

In order to sell books at a profit, the wholesaler buys in as large quantities and at as large discounts as possible. His gross profit is the very small difference between the discount received from the publisher and the discount given to the retailer, and out of this gross profit must come the wholesaler's own running expenses. As every publisher gives greater discounts for larger orders, the wholesaler naturally makes his orders as large as he believes is safe, and sometimes larger than proves to be safe. Depending on the book and other things, a first order will be for five, ten, fifteen, or twenty copies up to perhaps twenty-five thousand copies. Of necessity something of a gambler, the wholesaler is, however, a wary gambler. Through long and often sad experience, he knows in a general way what books will sell well, though no one can be absolutely sure of the book-buying public. By studying the market, the past records of the author, the special features of the book, the advertising to be given it, and trade conditions generally, the wholesaler arrives at an approximation of the number of copies he can probably sell in a few months' time. Sometimes, however, he has to overbuy deliberately in order to get a satisfactory discount or to render a special service to the publishers or to the retail booksellers. To help establish a new author, he will occasionally "plunge" on a book and do his best to make that book a success. And to help his customers he frequently stocks books upon which there is no profit, or perhaps even a loss, for he must carry the books of all publishers, regardless of his own profit on individual titles.

Indeed, to keep his stock representative of all publishers, he carries "on consignment" the books of many small publishers and acts as "sales agent" for some. He is their distributing center—and often their only point of contact with the retail shops. Without the wholesaler's aid they could exist—but not so well.

The actual purchase of books does not end the responsibilities of the wholesaler's buyer. He must see to it that books are re-ordered whenever stock is getting low, and to do this he must keep a record of the sales of each book. As it is quite usual for the important jobber to carry as many as 50,000 different titles in stock, this record keeping is an extremely complicated task in itself. There must be a record card for each book, upon which the quantity on hand is entered at regular intervals. This information is obtained by an actual count of stock, the total of which often reaches hundreds of thousands of books. Then the 50,000 cards have to be consulted constantly and checked just as constantly. The publisher's price changes and discount changes, when they occur, must be noted immediately. If the book is out of stock when it is re-ordered from the publisher, this fact must be noted so the order can be sent in later. If too many copies of a book have been purchased, the overstock has to be disposed of in some manner, such as by selling it in bulk, persuading the publisher to take it back, or even reducing the price.

In order to create a demand for his stock of books, the wholesaler circularizes his customers regularly. While he cannot afford to advertise individual titles, he can and does use the publisher's advertising material to good advantage. When a "best seller" is to be published, the publisher usually prints letters to the trade, post cards, and circulars, and he then can supply the wholesaler with as many of these as the importance of the book warrants. Such publicity material of course, bears the wholesaler's name, and it is sent to his picked list of bookstores and individual buyers—and in consequence both he and the publisher benefit. Mr. Stanley Unwin, in "The Truth About Publishing," declares that this direct mail advertising is extremely valuable. Because of the book wholesaler's close relations with the retailers his circularizing is particularly profitable, though it is, however, difficult to tell just how many sales a given effort produces.

In addition to such co-operative advertising, the wholesaler's publicity department prepares catalogs and special book lists, containing information about forthcoming books, so that the customers can find all the best new titles in one list and place their orders accordingly. Even bookshops which buy directly from publishers sometimes make use of these lists. The wholesaler also issues once a year a general catalog of standard and new books, including all those which the retailers usually carry in stock. These catalogs are almost indispensable to the retail booksellers, because they rely to such a great extent upon the wholesaler's experience and knowledge. Indeed, the wholesaler frequently suggests to booksellers and to rental library proprietors just what their initial stock orders should be, including both how many copies of each book and even the titles themselves. For this reason the wholesaler's influence can often "make" a book, but although he is glad to help when a title is really worthy, the possible injury to his customers and to himself because of loss of their confidence prevents his pushing an unworthy volume.

After the demand has been created by advance advertising and by salesmen, the orders begin to come in; these have to be deciphered, and the books shipped. The word "deciphered" is not used here in jest, for it is often impossible to make out what the customer wants. Intelligent retail booksellers weed out all the mistakes they can from the orders of the individual buyer, but they are glad to pass the riddles on to the jobber. Thus orders often come in giving titles without authors, authors without titles, and sometimes for a vague title which was "reviewed in the *Times* last Sunday or the week before." One bookseller once actually requested "Boni Librit, by Bitriss Shensi," meaning, of course, the Boni & Liveright edition of "Beatrice Cenci." This mistake seems incredible, but it is of a kind by no means rare.

As the depository for the books of all publishers, the wholesaler has so long been called upon to fill obscure orders that his facilities for locating a given book are almost unbelievably complete. All the "tools of the trade"—catalogs, lists, files, indexes—are kept on hand so that given either the title or the author's name, he can usually identify a book. Part of this ability lies in knowing where to look for the information, and the rest depends upon memory, an active imagination, and a certain "feel" that all good bookmen acquire. While the wholesaler is widely known for his ability in solving such puzzles, it is not a profitable part of his work. Some booksellers indeed abuse his patience by ordering nothing but titles which they themselves do not recognize.

To fill all reasonable orders the wholesaler maintains a stock of tens of thousands of volumes. His is a sort of "reserve" upon which bookstores can draw to supplement their own stock and, therefore, he must be able to ship immediately any and all the titles likely to be asked for at the retail shops. And not only must this immense stock be instantly available, but also the orders must be packed and shipped a few hours after they have been received. Probably this service is the chief advantage of buying books from the wholesaler; he has under one roof practically all titles in current demand and can often ship them much more quickly than the publishers themselves. About 9000 new books are published each year, of which a retail bookseller can stock from 500 to 1000 only; so if he were not able to supply any of the others upon short notice, he would lose many of his customers.

A retail dealer often wants a book or two from each of a dozen publishers in Boston, New York, Chicago, Philadelphia, or some other cities. Instead of sending a dozen orders and having to pay as many charges for shipping, he sends one order to the wholesaler and receives his books quickly, in one shipment, with a minimum risk of delay, loss, or damage.

The jobber, then, sells more than books; he sells service. He locates books, he "rushes" shipments, he selects profitable stock for rental libraries and shops, he keeps his customers informed of new books, he arranges to have important books in the book shops before publication, and he is always ready to give his customers the advantage of the knowledge which comes from his long experience.

As the wholesaler's prosperity depends upon the prosperity of his customers, he naturally keeps a watchful eye on them. If a book shop is inclined to reckless buying or shows declining vitality, the wholesaler tactfully inquires into the matter. Sometimes he can save a shop from ruin by prompt intervention. He may suggest remedies. Occasionally he disposes of overstock.

He sometimes finds a purchaser for a book shop, or a book shop for a purchaser. It goes without saying that he always is ready to supply his customers with such trade helps as posters, catalogs, and circulars. He may even lend the services of his own advertising and editorial departments to help a customer to plan advertising or to lay out a circular. In short, he does his best to make book shops thrive and multiply in the land.

SELLING BY SUBSCRIPTION

By Charles S. Olcott

THE business of selling books may be divided, in a general way, into two divisions, one seeking to bring the people to the books, the other aiming to take the books to the people. The first operates through the retail book stores, news-stands, department stores, and the like. The other employs agents, or advertises in the newspapers or magazines, to secure orders or "subscriptions," on receipt of which the books are delivered. The latter method of selling has become known as the "Subscription-book" business.

The agent usually calls at the office or home of his prospective customer and shows samples of the text pages, illustrations, bindings, etc., bound together in a form known as a "prospectus." Sometimes he exhibits a number of different prospectuses. The customer signs an order blank, which the agent turns over to the publisher, who makes the delivery and collects the money. To cover the entire country, the large publisher establishes branch offices in many different cities or sells his books to so-called "general agents," who secure their own canvassers.

It may be asked, why does such a method exist? Do

not people know enough to go to the book stores and ask for what they want? And why go to a man and urge him to buy a book he does not want? The answer goes deep into human nature. People have to be urged to take very many things which they know they ought to have. The small boy knows he ought to go to school, but has to be coaxed. Parents know he ought to go, but compulsory education laws have been found necessary in many states. The churches are good, but people sometimes need urging even to go there. Life insurance, honestly conducted, is one of the greatest blessings a man can buy with money, but the principal expenditures of the great companies are the vast sums spent in pleading with the people to take advantage of it.

Experience has proved this to be true of books. Men and women must be employed to show the people their value. The latest novel, if popular and well advertised, will sell fairly well in the retail store, but an encyclopædia, or any extensive set of books, must be taken directly to the people and explained by competent salesmen if the publishers hope to pay the cost of the plates within a lifetime. This is strikingly illustrated by the experience of a large publishing house which made beautiful new plates of the writings of several famous authors and offered the editions to the book stores, only to find that the book stores did not sell them and that valuable publishing rights were in danger of dying on their hands. They decided to organize a department to sell the books by subscription. This was more than a generation ago.

The sale immediately revived, increased to proportions never before achieved, and continues to the present day.

Forty or fifty years ago, by far the most common form of subscription book was the variety labelled "Manual of Business," or the "Complete Farm Cyclopedia," or the "Road to Heaven." The publisher did not advertise for customers but for agents. The books were sold directly to the agent, and he in turn delivered them to his customers and collected the money. Anybody out of employment could take up the business. The aim was to get as many agents as possible and sell them the books. The agent canvassed with a "prospectus" after committing to memory his little story. The subscribers signed their names in the back of the prospectus. Sometimes the young and inexperienced agent ordered as many copies as he had signatures or more. Woe unto him if he did, for oftentimes they would not "deliver." Many years ago I remember calling at a modest little home in the Middle West. While waiting in the parlor, I noticed how peculiarly it was furnished. Every corner of the little square room contained a monument of symmetrical design, all different, but each some three or four feet high, and all built of books, as a child might build a fairy castle out of his wooden blocks. A closer inspection showed that all the volumes were copies of the same book bound in "half morocco"! The explanation came later when I was incidentally informed that "Willie had tried canvasssing, but most of 'em backed out."

This reminds one of the remark of Thoreau when, four years after the publication of his first book (at the author's expense), the publisher compelled him to remove 706 unsold copies out of the edition of 1000, and he had them all carted to his home. "I now have," he said, "a library of nearly 900 volumes, over 700 of which I wrote myself." It is an interesting fact in this connection that the successors of that publisher are today, fifty years later, successfully selling by subscription an edition of Thoreau's writings in 20 volumes, the set in the cheapest style of binding costing $100.

Among the famous books sold by this method have been Blaine's "Twenty Years in Congress," Stanley's "In Darkest Africa," many volumes by Mark Twain and Grant's "Memoirs." The handsome fortune which the publishers of the latter were enabled to pay to Mrs. Grant was made possible only by the application of the subscription method of reaching the people.

Another form of subscription book, now fortunately obsolete, was the book in "parts." A "part" consisted of some twenty-four or forty-eight pages, or more, in paper covers. These were delivered and paid for by the buyer in instalments of one or two at a time until the entire work was complete. Then the binding order was solicited. It was an expensive and unsatisfactory makeshift, intended to reach those who could pay only a dollar or two a month. The theory was that the people could not be trusted, and therefore the book must be cut up and delivered in pieces. Later the publishers learned that "most people are honest," and the modern method is to deliver the complete publication and collect the price in monthly instalments. This plan has proved far more economical both to subscribers and publishers, and the losses are few if the management is careful and conservative. One house which carefully scrutinizes its orders has suffered losses of less than one per cent on a business of several millions of dollars covering a period of over thirty years.

In late years by far the greatest part of the subscription-book business has been done with complete sets of books, reference sets or the writings of the standard authors. These books are sold directly to the subscriber who gives a signed order, and the publisher makes the delivery, pays the agent a cash commission, and collects the payments as they fall due. The old, worthless, "made-up" books are rapidly disappearing, and the subscription-book of today is as a rule a vastly superior article to that of years ago. In fact some of the oldest and most reliable publishing houses in America now offer their choicest output by subscription. A large investment of capital in plates, illustrations, editorial work, etc., such as is necessary in many of the extensive editions of standard works, could not be made unless there were an assured return. The subscription method of selling makes such undertakings possible, and the result of its adoption has been the issue of many superb publications which never would or could have been undertaken, had the retail book store been the only outlet to the market. The subscription business has in this way proved a marked benefit to the lovers of fine editions of their favorite authors. The booklover has been benefited, too, in the matter of prices. The agent's commission under the modern methods is no greater than the bookseller's profit, and no extraordinary allowance is made for losses, as many imagine, because the losses are comparatively small. The desire to extend his business leads the publisher to make his books more attractive, while there is plenty of competition to keep the prices down. It is a fact that the buyer is today getting a far better book for his money than ever before.

The personnel of the canvassing force has also undergone a change. A business such as the best houses are now doing requires agents of intelligence, tact, and judgment. The callow youth cannot succeed as he did once. The man who has failed at everything else will fail here. There are now men and women engaged in selling books by subscription, who possess business ability of a high order. Many of them have well-established lines of trade—regular customers who depend upon them to supply their wants and keep them informed. The old jibes about the book-agent fall flat when applied to them. They do not bore their customers nor tire them out. They serve them, and the customers are glad to be served by them.

I have taken care to point out that these observations apply to the business as conducted by the older and more conservative book publishers, who value their reputation.

In a consideration of the subject a sharp distinction should be drawn between such publishers and a class of irresponsible schemers who by various ingenious devices seek to gain the public ear and then proceed to impose upon their victims to the full extent of their credulity. In recent years many schemes have been devised—a few honest, some about half honest, and the rest miserable "fakes."

One of the earliest and most successful "schemes," not dishonest but certainly ingenious, was that of a publisher who had a large stock of unmarketable books whose retail price was $6 a volume. He organized an association and sold memberships at $10, the membership entitling the subscriber to one of the $6 books and the privilege of buying miscellaneous books at a discount. The discounts really were no greater than could have been obtained in any department store, but the "association" thought it had a great concession and multiplied so rapidly that the unmarketable book had to be reprinted again and again.

The next "scheme" to come into prominence was the so-called "raised contract." The process was simple. The order blank read, for example, $5 a volume, but the publisher wanted "a few influential citizens like yourself" to write testimonials, and had a few copies for sale to such people—only a very few—at $3, merely the cost of the paper and binding. By paying cash you could get another reduction, and as a special favor from the agent still another, and so on, until you found the price whittled down to the ridiculously low sum of $2.65. When the customer woke up and found that all his neighbors were also "influential citizens" who had bought at the same price or possibly less, and that the book would be dear at $2, he mentally resolved to "buy no more from that house." The figures are given merely to illustrate the idea and are not quoted from any particular proposition. It is unfortunately true, however, that the plan here illustrated or, various modifications of it, are even now in daily use by some concerns, although there are indications that it is gradually dying as the result of overwork!

Another scheme is to advertise "a few slightly damaged" copies of a book for sale at barely the cost of the sheets—to save rebinding. A publisher once confided to me that he was doing a "land-office business" selling "slightly damaged stock." "How do you damage the stock," I asked,—"throw the books across the room?" "No," he replied, laughing, "we haven't the time to do that."

Some of the schemes are so ludicrous as to cause one to wonder how anybody can be made to believe the story. Such was the one which soberly informed the prospective customer that he had been selected by a committee of Congress as one of a few representative citizens to whom the United States government would be willing to sell some of its precious documents. He was not asked to subscribe, but merely to "let us know" if he didn't want it, for "another gentleman" was quite anxious to secure his copy, etc.   Of course the fortunate representative citizen made haste to secure the copy which Congress intended him to have.   I am told that the originator of this scheme made a fortune out of it.

All these schemes, from the laughably absurd to the contemptibly mean, should be regarded merely as an excrescence upon the legitimate subscription-book business.   They are like the "get-rich-quick" and "wildcat" banking schemes which flourish in prosperous times, but have nothing whatever in common with legitimate financial affairs.   It is unfortunate for the book trade that these schemers selected books as the particular kind of merchandise upon which to exercise their ingenuity. They admit that their agents are expected not to canvass the merits of the book, but to "sell their story."   They might have done the same thing had they chosen jewelry, bric-à-brac, rugs, paintings, stocks, bonds, or anything else as the subject for their exploitation.   The reliable publishers are hoping that at no distant date the schemers will take up some of these other lines, although they bear no grudge against the latter.

If any prejudice exists in the public mind against subscription books, it is caused by the illegitimate use of books as a means of "fooling" if not of swindling the people.   There are many honorable men and many houses of the highest class who are engaged in the subscription-book business.   The intelligent and honorable book agent who represents a thoroughly reliable publishing house deserves to be differentiated from the fellow who comes with a lie on his tongue, for which an un-scrupulous schemer is directly responsible.

The subscription-book business, in the hands of honorable men, has performed a great service to the whole country, by putting good books into thousands and hundreds of thousands of homes, where, but for them, there would be little to read beyond the newspaper or the magazine. The best publishers have found it the most practicable method of distribution for their more extensive productions, and thousands of thoughtful men are glad of the opportunity to receive the representa-tives of such houses and to have the best of the new pub-lications promptly brought to their attention.

SELECTING FOR A PUBLIC LIBRARY

By Arthur E. Bostwick

IN selecting books for a public library, the two things
generally taken into account are the public desire
and the public need. The different values attached to
each of these two factors may be said to determine the
policy of the library in book-buying. The extreme cases,
where full force is given to one factor while the other
is entirely disregarded, do not, of course, exist. Libraries
do not purchase every book that is asked for, without
considering whether such purchases are right and proper.
Nor do they, on the other hand, disregard popular demand altogether and purchase from a list made up solely
with regard to what the community ought to read rather
than what it wants to read. Between these two extremes,
however, there may be an indefinite number of means.
A librarian may, for instance, purchase chiefly books in
general demand, exercising judgment in disregarding
such requests as he may deem improper. Or he may buy
chiefly those books that in his opinion should be read in
his community, listening to the voice of the public only
when it becomes importunate. Several considerations
may have part in influencing his course in this regard.
In the first place, a library with plenty of money at com-

mand may in a measure follow both plans; in other
words, it may buy not only all the good books that the
public wants to read, but those also that it should read.
The more limited the appropriation for book purchase,
the more pressing becomes the need that the librarian
should decide on a precise policy. Again, a library whose
books are for general circulation would naturally give
more heed to popular demand than a reference library
used chiefly by students. Further, an endowed institution, not dependent on public support, could afford to
disregard the public wishes to an extent impossible in
the case of a library whose expenses are paid by the
municipality from the proceeds of taxation. Above and
beyond all these considerations, the personal equation
comes in, sometimes very powerfully. It often seems as
if some library authorities regard popular favor as an
actual mark of discredit, while others look upon it almost
as a condition precedent to purchase. Take, as an
example, the so-called "fiction question," over which
most libraries, and some of their patrons, are at present
more or less exercised. There can be no doubt of the
popular regard for this form of literature, especially for
the current novel or romance. Some libraries would
sternly discourage this preference and refuse to purchase
fiction less than one year old, while others do not hesitate
to buy, within the limits of their purses, all such books
as would be likely to interest or entertain the average
reader of taste and intelligence. The views of the
selector regarding the relative importance of the library's

duties as an educator and an entertainer must also affect
his views.

It has been tacitly assumed that the selection is made
by one person. As a matter of fact, however, the final
approval is generally given by a book committee of some
kind, usually a committee of the library trustees or persons responsible to them, often with the help of outside
advisers. The weight of the librarian's views with this
body will depend on various circumstances. Sometimes
he has his own way; sometimes his wishes are practically
disregarded. Moreover, the composition of such a body
varies so that any continuous policy is difficult for it.

Owing to all these facts, it is probable that no two
libraries in the United States, even when they are closely
related by classification, as when both are branch libraries
for circulation, state libraries, public reference libraries,
or university libraries, are pursuing exactly the same
policy in book purchase, although, as has been said, their
various policies are always compounded of different proportions of these two factors—regard for the wishes and
demands of their users, and consideration of what is right
and proper for those users, from whatever standpoint.
The stickler for uniformity will lament this diversity,
but it is probably a good thing. In many libraries, there
are as many minds as there are men, and it cannot be
and ought not to be otherwise.

Now, how does the person or the group, that is responsible for the selection of books for a library ascertain
the facts on which, as has been said, the selection must

be based? It is usually not difficult to find out what the public wants. Its demands almost overwhelm the assistant at the desk. Some libraries provide special blank forms on which these requests may be noted. They are often capricious; sometimes they do not represent the dominant public wish. The voice of one insistent person asking for his book day after day may impress itself on the mind more forcibly than the many diffident murmurs of a considerable number. In libraries that possess a system of branches, there is little difficulty in recognizing a general public demand. Such a demand will be reported from a large number of branch libraries at once, in which case the chances of mistake will be small. In some libraries useful suggestions are gained through the operation of an inter-branch loan system, whereby a user of one branch may send for a book contained in any other branch. Books so asked for are reported at the central headquarters, and if they are not in the library at all, the request is regarded as a suggestion for purchase. Should such requests come from users of several branches at once, the desired book is very likely to be purchased. Often the demand is general rather than specific, as for "a book about the Caucasus" or for "more works on surveying," and sometimes they are vague or misleading, titles being wrong and authors' names spelled phonetically; yet the work made necessary in looking up these demands is more than repaid by the knowledge that it may result in making the library of more value to the public.

In some cases the librarian desires not only to respond to the public want, but even to anticipate it. He does not wait to see whether a new book on Japan will be in demand because he is sure that such will be the case. He does not hesitate to order a new book by a popular novelist, or the autobiography of an eminent citizen, as soon as he sees its title in the publisher's announcements. The necessity for some other anticipatory orders may be less evident, and this kind of work requires good judgment and discrimination; but in general if a book is to be purchased on publication, it cannot be on the library shelves too soon after the date of issue. In any case, where it is desirable and proper to please the public, double pleasure can be given by promptness; hence the importance of being a little before, rather than a little behind, the popular desire.

All this calls for little but quick and discriminating observation—the ability to feel and read the public pulse in matters literary. It is in regard to the second and more important factor that failure waits most insistently on the librarian. What are the public's needs, as distinguished from its desires? What ought it to read? Here steps in the "categorical imperative" with a vengeance. The librarian, when he thinks of his duty along this line, begins to shudder as he realizes his responsibility as an educator, as a mentor, as a trainer of literary taste. Probably in some instances he takes himself too seriously. But, no matter how lightly he may bear these responsibilities, every selector of books for a public library realizes that he must give some consideration to this question. In the first place, there are general needs; there are certain standard books that must be on the shelves of every well-ordered library, no matter whether they are read or not. It is his business to provide and recommend them. What are these standards? No two lists are alike. They start together: "the Bible and Shakespeare"—and then off they go in divergent paths! Secondly, there are special needs dependent on locality or on the race or temperament of the users of a particular library. The determination of these needs in itself is a task of no small magnitude; their legitimate satisfaction is sometimes difficult in the extreme. To take a concrete instance, the librarian may discover that there is in his vicinity a little knot of people who meet occasionally to talk over current questions, not formally, but half by accident. They would be benefited, and would be greatly interested, in the right sort of books on economics, but they have scarcely heard that there is such a subject. That the public library might be interested in them and might aid them would never occur to any of them. The discovery of such people, the determination of just what books they need, and the successful bringing together of man and book—all these are the business of the librarian, and it is a part of his work that cannot be separated from that of book selection.

In much of this work the librarian of a large library must depend to a great extent on others. Both the desires and the needs of those who use his library he must learn from the reports of subordinates and from outside friends. The librarian of a small library can ascertain much personally; but both librarians are largely dependent upon expert opinion in their final selections. After concluding that the library must have an especially full and good collection of books on pottery, the selector must go to some one who knows, to find out what are the best works on this subject. When there is a good list, he must know where to find it, or at least where to go to find out where it is. He must consult all the current publishers' lists as they appear, and scan each catalog of bargains. His list of books wanted for purchase should far exceed his ability to buy, for then he must, perforce, exercise his judgment and pick out the best. If, after all, the collection of books in his library is not such as to meet the approval of the public, he must bow meekly under the weight of its scorn.

The deluge of books that falls daily from the presses is almost past comprehension. The number of intelligent readers, thanks to the opportunities given by our public libraries, is increasing in due proportion. To select from the stream what is properly fitted to the demands of this rapidly growing host is a task not to be lightly performed. That the authorities of our libraries do not shrink from it is fortunate indeed; that the result is no worse than it is, is a fact on which the reading public must doubtless be congratulated.